CIRIA C506

London, 1998

Low-cost options for prevention of flooding from sewers

R W P May

P Martin

N J Price

CIRIA *sharing knowledge ■ building best practice*

6 Storey's Gate, Westminster, London SW1P 3AU
TELEPHONE 0171 222 8891   FAX 0171 222 1708
EMAIL switchboard@ciria.org.uk
WEBSITE www.ciria.org.uk

Summary

The risk that properties may experience flooding from sewers is a key issue for the owners and occupiers of the properties, for the sewerage undertakers in the UK, and for the water industry regulator, Ofwat. Some flooding problems can be dealt with by carrying out construction works that upgrade the overall capacity of the sewerage system. In other cases it may not be possible to justify the cost of major works on the basis of the benefits that will result for a limited number of properties. In these types of situation, alternative low-cost methods of preventing flooding from sewers can therefore play an important role in providing protection for at-risk properties.

This guidance document summarises the results of a CIRIA project in which low-cost options for preventing flooding from sewers were identified and information collected on their suitability and effectiveness. The document is aimed at the needs of drainage engineers and planners working for sewerage undertakers, local authorities, contractors and developers.

CIRIA C506

Low-cost options for prevention of flooding from sewers.
Construction Industry Research and Information Association

ISBN 0-86017-506-5
© CIRIA 1998

Keywords		
Sewers, flooding, prevention, low-cost methods		
Reader interest	**Classification**	
Engineers responsible for planning, designing, constructing, or maintaining drainage works	AVAILABILITY CONTENT STATUS USER	Unrestricted Guidance document Committee-guided Drainage engineers

Foreword

This guidance document is the final output from the research project *Low-cost options for prevention of flooding from sewers*, which forms part of CIRIA's water engineering programme. The principal objective of the project was to produce a guidance document to inform sewerage undertakers and other interested parties about the options that are available and the situations in which they can appropriately be used.

The work steps that were carried out in order to produce the guidance document were as follows:

1. Analysis of the number and causes of sewer-related flooding incidents in the UK.

2. Collection of quantitative and qualitative data on different options for preventing flooding from sewers, taking into consideration UK and overseas practice and new developments.

3. Appraisal of different options, taking account (where data were available) of capital costs, maintenance costs, reliability and range of suitability.

4. Consideration of external constraints affecting the selection and maintenance of different options for prevention of flooding, including Building Regulations, planning issues, Ofwat requirements and legal aspects.

The report was written under contract to CIRIA by Mr Richard May of HR Wallingford, Mr Peter Martin of Binnie Black & Veatch and Mr Nicholas Price of TPS Consult. Following CIRIA's established practice, the research project was guided by a steering group, which comprised:

Mr John Blanskby (Chairman)	Sheffield Hallam University
Mr Ian Abram	North West Water
Dr Robert Andoh	Hydro Research and Development Ltd
Mr Peter Forster	Southern Water Services
Mr Mark Hann	Office of Water Services (Ofwat)
Mr Frederick Keatley	Water Service (Northern Ireland)
Mr Carl Michalski	New Forest District Council
Mr Martin Osborne	Reid Crowther Consulting Ltd
Mr Don Ridgers	Thames Water Utilities
Mr Jim Street	South West Water
Mr David Wilson	West of Scotland Water

Additional corresponding members of the Steering Group were:

Mr Robert Kerr	Scottish Environment Protection Agency (SEPA)
Mr David Knowles	Office of Water Services (Ofwat)

CIRIA's research manager for the project was Mr Richard Lillywhite. The project was funded by:

Institution of Civil Engineers
North West Water
Scottish Association of Directors of Water and Sewerage Services
South West Water
Southern Water Services
Thames Water Utilities
Water Service (Northern Ireland)

Contents

FIGURES

TABLES

Glossary

anti-flooding device   A device specifically designed to be installed in gravity drains or sewers to prevent backflow from a sewer towards a property or group of properties.

best management practices   Structural and non-structural measures used to store or treat urban surface water runoff to reduce flooding, remove pollution and provide other amenities.

blockage   A deposit in a sewer or drain resulting in a restriction of the flow.

combined system   A drain or sewer system designed to carry both wastewater and surface water in the same pipeline(s).

combined sewer overflow   A structure on a combined or partially separate sewer system that allows flows above a prescribed limit to be discharged to another sewer, to a storm-water retention tank, to a watercourse, or to another disposal point.

drain   A pipeline, usually underground, designed to carry wastewater and/or surface water from a source to a sewer; a pipeline carrying land drainage flows or surface water from a highway.

foul sewage   Waterborne waste of domestic or industrial origin excluding rainwater and surface water.

foul system   A drain or sewer system that has been designed to carry only wastewater.

gravity system   A drain or sewer system where flow is caused by the force of gravity and where the pipeline is designed normally to operate partially full.

Guaranteed Standards Scheme   A compensation scheme operating in England and Wales under which water service companies make payments to customers if certain standards of service specified by Ofwat are not met.

highway   Any road, track, bridleway or public footpath in private or public ownership that is not associated with an individual property.

highway drainage system   A drain or sewer system constructed for the purpose of draining a highway.

infiltration (to sewer)   The ingress of groundwater into a drain or sewer system through defects in pipes, joints or manholes.

interceptor sewer   A large, often very flat, sewer built to intercept and convey flows from several trunk sewers.

invert   The bottom of the inside of a pipe or conduit.

lateral	A private drain carrying drainage flows from a property to a public sewer.
malconnection	An incorrect connection of an inlet or drain to a drain or sewer that is not designed to carry that element of flow (eg foul sewage entering a surface water system or surface water entering a separate foul system).
manhole	A chamber with a removable cover constructed on a drain or sewer to permit entry by personnel.
partially separate system	A drain or sewer system, normally of two pipelines, where one pipeline carries wastewater together with a designed quantity of surface water and the other pipeline carries the balance of the surface water.
pressure sewerage system	A system that operates under positive pressure to pump drainage flows from a property or group of properties into a public sewer; the system may consist of one or more pumps, storage chambers, pipework and non-return valves.
private drain	A drain for which responsibility is not vested with the sewerage undertaker.
public sewer	A sewer for which responsibility is vested with the sewerage undertaker.
rider sewer	A gravity sewer that collects drainage flow from a group of properties and conveys it to a pumping station or to a connection with a sewer further downstream.
runoff	Water from precipitation that flows off a surface to reach a drain, sewer or receiving water.
Section 24 sewer	A drain serving two or more properties, the responsibility for which was transferred from a private owner to a sewerage undertaker as a result of legislation (ie Section 24 of the 1936 Public Health Act and later legislation). See Section 2.2 of Chapter 2 for more details, including specific legislation relating to London.
separate system	A drain or sewer system, normally of two pipelines, one carrying wastewater and the other surface water.
sewage	Wastewater and/or surface water conveyed by a drain or sewer.
sewer	A pipe or conduit that conveys wastewater and/or surface water.
sewer flooding	The unintentional escape of sewage from a sewerage system; the inability of drainage flows to enter a sewerage system because of surcharging. (see also Section 5.1 for alternative definitions).

sewerage system	A network of pipelines and ancillary works that conveys wastewater and/or surface water from drains to a treatment works or other place of disposal.
sewerage undertaker	An organisation with the legal duty to provide sewerage services in an area. In England and Wales these services are provided by 10 water service companies, in Scotland by three water authorities, and in Northern Ireland by the Water Service of the Department of the Environment for Northern Ireland.
soffit	The top of the inside of a pipe or conduit.
surcharge	The condition in which wastewater and/or surface water is held under pressure within a gravity drain or sewer system, but does not escape to the surface to cause flooding.
surface water	Water from precipitation that has not seeped into the ground and that is discharged to the drain or sewer system directly from the ground or from exterior building surfaces.
surface water system	A drain or sewer system that has been designed to carry only surface water.
vacuum sewerage system	A system that operates under negative (sub-atmospheric) pressure to evacuate drainage flows from a property or group of properties; the system may consist of one or more vacuum pumps, a central vacuum reservoir, pipework and interface valves.
wastewater	Water changed by use and discharged to a drain or sewer system.

Abbreviations

AFD	anti-flooding device
AMP	asset management plan
BMP	best management practices
BS	British Standard
CCTV	closed-circuit television
CEN	Comité Européen de Normalisation (European Committee for Standardisation)
CSO	combined sewer overflow
DG	director general of Ofwat
DG5	Register 5 of the annual report by the director general of Ofwat dealing with flooding from sewers
EN	Europäische Norm (European Standard)
pr EN	provisional EN
GIS	geographical information system
GLC	Greater London Council
GRP	glass-reinforced plastic
GSS	Guaranteed Standards Scheme
LCC	London County Council
Ofwat	Office of Water Services for England and Wales
PS	pumping station
PSS	pressure sewerage system
SU	sewerage undertaker
UKWIR	UK Water Industry Research Limited
WC	water closet

Background information

1 Introduction

1.1 SCOPE

The risk that properties may experience flooding from sewers is a key issue for the owners and occupiers of the properties, for the sewerage undertakers, and for the water industry regulator Ofwat. The most commonly adopted solution for dealing with sewer flooding problems involves carrying out construction works in the sewerage system to increase the flow capacity. However, this approach may not be appropriate if the cost of the works is too high in relation to the number of properties that will be safeguarded from flooding. Also, the time span associated with the investigation, design and construction of new drainage works can often be of the order of five or more years, during which the affected properties remain at risk of flooding. There is therefore a need to consider alternatives to construction works that may be more cost-effective or that can be implemented more quickly to provide the public with worthwhile improvements in the level of service.

The principal objective of this CIRIA project was to produce a guidance document to inform sewerage undertakers and other interested parties about the options that are available and the situations in which they can appropriately be used. The project considered all types of sewer flooding problem, whether inside or outside buildings or whether due to lack of sewer capacity or to other causes such as blockages.

1.2 HOW TO USE THIS DOCUMENT

The document is divided into three main parts as follows:

- **Background information**

  This part will be of use as an introduction when reading the document for the first time. The three chapters give an overall view of sewer-flooding problems in the UK and of the options that are available for prevention.

  Chapter 1. The scope and structure of the report are explained.

  Chapter 2. Information is provided on the numbers of properties in the UK that experience problems of flooding from sewers or are assessed to be at significant risk. Data are also given on the most common causes and types of flooding.

  Chapter 3. Outline descriptions are given of 11 low-cost options for preventing flooding from sewers. The conventional solution of carrying out construction works to increase sewer capacity is included as an additional option for comparison purposes.

- **Procedures for selecting and implementing options**

  This part contains the key information that needs to be considered by drainage engineers and planners when investigating particular sewer flooding problems and developing solutions. Chapter 8 contains the detailed selection criteria and is likely to be the most frequently used section of the text.

  Chapter 4. Details are given of various types and sources of data that should be consulted when first considering remedial measures for a particular sewer-flooding problem.

  Chapter 5. Guidance is provided here on how the data from Chapter 4 should be classified in order to define the nature of individual flooding problems, ie where they occur, how often and to what extent.

  Chapter 6. This describes the next step in the process, which is to identify the particular cause of the sewer flooding, eg whether it is due to hydraulic or non-hydraulic problems or whether further investigation is needed.

  Chapter 7. The choice of option for preventing sewer flooding may not be dictated solely by technical and economic factors. Information is given here on external constraints that may apply because of building and planning regulations or requirements set by water industry regulators.

  Chapter 8. Detailed criteria are given in this chapter for selecting suitable options for preventing flooding from sewers. This is done by considering four representative cases ranging in scale from problems affecting single basements to more widespread problems in sub-catchments. Information is given on maintenance requirements, and typical costs for each of the options are provided.

  Chapter 9. This chapter gives recommendations on how schemes for preventing flooding from sewers should be implemented and what types of arrangements are appropriate between sewerage undertakers and the owners or occupiers of the properties concerned.

- **Detailed technical data on options**

  Four appendices give more detailed technical data on the various options considered in the first two parts of the document.

  Appendix A1. Anti-flooding devices.

  Appendix A2. Pumping systems (pressure and vacuum).

  Appendix A3. Sewerage options.

  Appendix A4. Comparisons of costs and benefits for alternative options.

A considerable number of factors may need to be taken into account when investigating problems of sewer flooding and identifying suitable low-cost options for prevention. Figure 1 provides an overview of the way in which the various factors are interrelated.

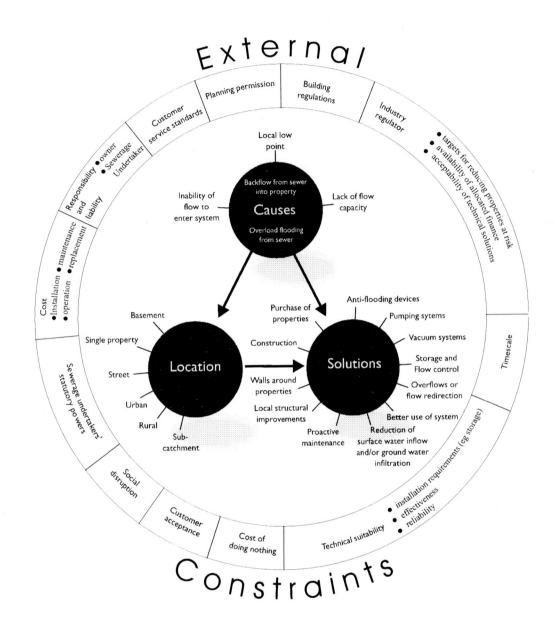

Figure 1.1 *Interrelationship between factors affecting selection of low-cost options*

2 Scale of sewer flooding problems in UK

2.1 OVERALL STATISTICS

In England and Wales, the director general (DG) of the Office of Water Services (Ofwat) requires sewerage undertakers to collect data on the numbers of properties that are flooded, or are at significant risk of being flooded, from public sewers. The statistics are submitted and published annually in Register 5 of the director general's report and are therefore referred to as DG5 statistics.

The statistics required by Ofwat are limited to cases of internal flooding in which any type of flow from a public sewer enters an occupied building or passes below a suspended floor. In this context, an occupied building is one that is used for residential, public, commercial, business or industrial purposes and is normally occupied. Flooding in an integral garage of an occupied property needs to be reported, but not flooding in an unoccupied garage that is detached or linked-detached. The following three types of data need to be provided by the sewerage undertakers in England and Wales to Ofwat:

(a) Any incidents of internal flooding of occupied properties from public sewers occurring during the period of record. Every incident must be reported, whatever the cause (eg lack of sewer capacity, equipment failures, blockages, collapses, etc).

(b) The number of occupied properties that are assessed to be at risk of flooding more frequently than twice in 10 years due to lack of sewer capacity.

(c) The number of occupied properties that are assessed to be at risk of flooding more frequently than once in 10 years but less frequently than twice in 10 years due to lack of sewer capacity.

Flooding problems affecting unoccupied buildings, gardens, open spaces and highways are not included; the relative proportions of these different types of incident are considered in Section 2.2. Also, the figures for at-risk properties (cases (b) and (c) above) refer only to those that are considered to be in danger of flooding because of lack of flow capacity in the sewers. Therefore, a property experiencing repeated flooding due to blockages may not necessarily be included in the figures even though the incidents may be the result of an underlying problem in the sewerage system.

In Table 2.1 statistics from the Ofwat Report[1] on levels of service for 1996–97 are given on the numbers of flooding incidents and the numbers of properties assessed to be at risk in England and Wales. The difference between each corresponding pair of numbers in categories 1 and 2 indicates how many properties suffered flooding for reasons other than lack of flow capacity in the sewers; such reasons can include local blockages, pumping station failures, burst rising mains, etc. It can be seen from Table 2.1 that the numbers of flooding incidents have reduced steadily since 1994; the proportion due to overloaded sewers was approximately 50% in the period 1992–95, but reduced to about 33% in 1996–97. The absolute numbers of flooding incidents caused by "other" factors (those not due to lack of flow capacity) have not significantly declined since 1995.

Table 2.1 *DG5 statistics of flooding from sewers for 1992–1997*

Category	Numbers of properties				
	1992–93	1993–94	1994–95	1995–96	1996–97
(1) Properties affected by internal flooding incidents	10 858	11 335	6825	5238	4627
(2) Properties in (1) affected because of overloaded sewers	4821	6476	3061	1980	1481
(3) Properties with risk of flooding more than twice in 10 years	~19 500	~19 500	~19 500	14 932	13 018
(4) Properties with risk of flooding between once and twice in 10 years	–	–	–	15 445	15 965

In the case of categories 3 and 4 in Table 2.1, the DG5 reporting requirements were changed in 1995–96 to include properties with flooding risks between once in 10 years and twice in 10 years. As a result, sewerage undertakers reassessed their records and assigned some properties from category 3 to the new category 4. The number of properties assessed to be in category 3 (ie with a risk of twice in 10 years or worse) has fallen by about 13% between 1995 and 1997, reflecting the efforts of sewerage undertakers to deal with serious problems of under-capacity in their systems. However, there has been a small increase in the number of properties in the lower-risk category 4; this may be partly due to reassignment of some properties from category 3 as a result of remedial works carried out.

It needs to be remembered that the figures in Table 2.1 do not include data for Scotland and Northern Ireland, which are not covered by DG5 reporting requirements. If it is assumed that the incidence of flooding problems per unit of population in these two countries is similar to that in England and Wales, it can be estimated that in 1996–97 the total numbers of properties at risk in the UK were approximately as follows:

Category 3	(≥ 2 times in 10 years)	14 600
Category 4	(1–2 times in 10 years)	17 900
Total		32 500

If no remedial actions were taken, it is likely that the numbers of properties assessed to be at risk of flooding from sewers would increase with time. This can be caused by changes of land use within catchments (leading sometimes to increased flows in the sewers) or to changes of building use (eg conversions of cellars to occupied basements).

2.2 DATA ON CAUSES OF FLOODING

Information obtained by May[2] from a survey of sewerage undertakers indicated that the most common causes of flooding from sewers were:

- inadequate flow capacity in public sewers
- random blockages in pipes and intercepting traps
- recurring blockages (due to characteristics of sewerage systems)
- inability of drainage flows from basements to enter public sewers
- pumping station failures
- burst rising mains
- high river or tide levels causing inflows to sewers
- siltation (due to flat sewer gradients or sewer features)
- fats and greases
- sewer collapses.

Other causes that have also been identified are:

- failures of screening equipment
- inadequate flow capacity in private drains
- inadequate flow capacity in culverted watercourses
- localised downstream restrictions in public sewers
- overland flows resulting from disruption of land drainage systems
- surface water entering foul or combined sewers
- infiltration of groundwater
- properties in local low spots.

In large cities, overloaded sewers typically account for approximately 50% of flooding problems – a much higher proportion than tends to apply in rural districts. This difference is partly due to the greater age of the sewerage systems in many inner-city areas and to the higher housing density, which can result in many properties being affected simultaneously. Also building developments around the perimeter of an urban area can increase flow rates in the core part of the sewerage system and thereby increase the frequency of flooding. Data for a major UK city suggest that about 50% of the at-risk properties are likely to experience above-ground flooding, while the other 50% are only in danger of below-ground flooding.

Many flooding problems are associated with Section 24 sewers. These were originally built as private drains but are now the responsibility of the sewerage undertakers. Section 24 of the 1936 Public Health Act placed an obligation on the relevant drainage authorities to carry out cleaning of all private drains that served two or more properties; this change applied to all such drains built before 1 October 1937. The 1989 Water Act and the 1991 Water Industry Act extended the obligation so that drainage authorities in England and Wales (and their successor organisations) became responsible for both repair and maintenance of Section 24 sewers. The London Government Act of 1963 resulted in all private drains built before 1 April 1965 within the area of the London County Council (LCC) being classified as Section 24 sewers. The drainage systems of some housing projects built outside London by the LCC (or the successor GLC) may also have been classified as Section 24 sewers.

Section 24 sewers tend to be troublesome because they were not necessarily constructed to the same standards as normal public sewers. In London, local legislation also resulted in many of them being fitted with intercepting traps, which increase the chances of blockages occurring.

A significant issue in urban areas can be the conversion of unoccupied cellars into basement dwellings. Sometimes the level of a basement floor may be below the soffit level of the public sewer, in which case the sewer does not even have to surcharge for flow to back up into the private drainage connection. Relaying a major sewer at a lower level in order to cater for a limited number of basement dwellings is unlikely to be cost-effective, so low-cost alternatives need to be considered in these types of situation.

Problems in rural areas and smaller towns are likely to be proportionately far fewer and different in nature. In the case of some sewerage undertakers, only about 10% or less of flooding incidents are identified as being due to lack of sewer capacity. Analysis of information on 3790 incidents held in one flood reporting system gave the following data on relative occurrences (smoothed and adjusted to take account of multiple or blank answers to some questions on the reporting form).

- Location
occupied buildings	7%
other buildings	3%
gardens	46%
open ground	20%
highways	24%

- Sewer type
combined	19%
foul	78%
surface water	2%
rising main	1%

- Cause of flooding
blockage	87%
overloaded sewer	6%
pumping station failure	2%
burst rising main	2%
other	3%

- Weather conditions
dry	81%
light rain	9%
heavy rain	10%

If attention is concentrated on the 6% of cases where flooding was due to sewer overloading, the relative occurrences were found to be as follows.

- Location
occupied buildings	13%
other buildings	9%
gardens	45%
open ground	16%
highways	17%

CIRIA C506

- Sewer type

combined	60%
foul	34%
surface water	6%
rising main	0%

- Weather conditions

dry	37%
light rain	8%
heavy rain	55%

A significant point from the above data is that flooding of occupied buildings represents only a small proportion of the total sewer flooding incidents. As expected, sewer overloading is most commonly associated with combined sewers, but, perhaps surprisingly, only with heavy rain in just over 50% of cases. It should be stressed that this analysis is based on records from a sewerage undertaker that does not serve large inner-city areas.

3   Options for preventing flooding from sewers

3.1   GENERAL

The following sections of this chapter briefly describe each of the alternative flood prevention methods identified from publications, discussions with UK sewerage undertakers and contacts with other organisations.

Some of the methods have been very little used in the UK or elsewhere, and no quantitative information on their effectiveness and reliability is therefore available. Some methods, such as "redirection of flows" or "provision of storage", are generic and their method of application depends very much on the specific site conditions. In these cases, only general descriptions can be given of their characteristics and of the situations in which they are likely to be effective.

More detailed information for each of the flood prevention options is provided in the following appendices:

- Appendix A1 – anti-flooding devices
- Appendix A2 – pumping systems (pressure and vacuum)
- Appendix A3 – sewerage options.

The topics covered include: technical standards; types of application; extent of usage; costs; and reliability/effectiveness.

3.2   ANTI-FLOODING DEVICES

Many mechanical devices are available for use in pipe systems to prevent flow reversal. In gravity drainage systems, check valves and external flap gates have sometimes been used, but neither type is fully suitable for this function.

Check valves are normally installed in pumping mains to prevent back-flow through the pumps and to mitigate shock pressures due to water hammer. The valves are usually heavy and robust, and therefore tend to produce undesirably high head losses if used in gravity systems.

External flap gates (often referred to as tide flaps) are most commonly installed at the downstream ends of surface water sewers to prevent flow entering them when river or tide levels are high. The externally hinged flap, usually of metal, plastic or rubber, can be attached to the end of a pipe, to a headwall or to an internal wall of a manhole. Rubber duckbill devices that squeeze flat when the downstream pressure exceeds the upstream pressure are also included in this category. External flap gates are less suitable for use within gravity drainage systems because head differences may not be large enough for them to seal positively if the flow contains grit, rag or faecal solids.

In this report, the term anti-flooding device (AFD) is reserved for backflow preventers specifically designed for use in gravity drains or sewers. These are normally in-line devices that have low head-loss characteristics and a good resistance to blockage. The method of closure that prevents backflow can take a variety of forms, including flap gates, gate valves or ball valves, either singly or in combination.

Since this report does not recommend check valves and external flap gates for normal in-line use in gravity drainage systems, Appendix A1 provides detailed information only on anti-flooding devices.

3.3 PUMPING SYSTEMS

Pumping systems for dealing with sewer-flooding problems can be considered in three categories of size and complexity.

(1) Packaged systems, consisting of pumps and storage chambers that can take gravity flow from a group of properties and, if necessary, pump it under pressure into a surcharged public sewer (either directly or via a gravity pipe).

(2) Intermediate-size pumps installed in inspection chambers that can discharge flow from a single property or basement into a surcharged sewer (either directly or via a gravity pipe).

(3) Small macerating pumps with small-bore pipework that can discharge flow under pressure from individual units such as baths, sinks, WCs and showers. Higher-rated units are able to pump from below ground level into surcharged sewers, either directly or via a gravity pipe.

Pumps used for categories (1) and (2) are normally either small submersibles with macerators or grinder pumps.

3.4 VACUUM SYSTEMS

These systems transport sewage by inducing and maintaining a vacuum in the collecting pipes by means of central vacuum pumps and a reservoir. Conventional gravity drains connect one or more properties to a sewage collection chamber. When the sewage reaches a preset level, a pneumatic "interface" valve opens and the contents of the chamber are sucked into the vacuum line. When the chamber is almost empty the valve closes.

Vacuum systems should normally deal only with domestic wastewater because satisfactory performance depends on their being sized accurately in relation to the maximum design rate of flow. These systems should not be expected to cater for overland flow, infiltration or roof run-off, and additional flows should not be added without considering the limitations of the original design.

3.5 LOCAL STRUCTURAL IMPROVEMENTS

Surcharging in lengths of sewer can sometimes be caused by local restrictions in sewers or manholes. Examples include lateral connections that project into a main sewer and thereby cause blockages, or poor benching in manholes that produces extra head losses or backing up of flow in side branches. Once these types of restriction have been located, they can usually be remedied at a relatively low cost.

3.6 REDUCTION/ATTENUATION OF SURFACE WATER INFLOWS AND REDUCTION OF INFILTRATION

This covers methods aimed at attenuating or reducing inflows into a sewerage system. Many are widely recognised as source control techniques or, in US terminology, as best management practices (BMPs). Examples of these techniques include:

- attenuation of roof runoff

- disconnection of paved areas and/or roof areas

- reductions in the numbers of gullies and stormwater inlets

- control of inflow rates at gullies

- reduction of infiltration into the sewerage system

- identification and correction of malconnections.

It should be noted that sewerage undertakers in England and Wales are not able to impose any restrictions on highway authorities concerning amounts of surface water input to their systems, whereas in Scotland limitations can be applied.

The source control techniques above are discussed in these CIRIA publications:

- CIRIA Report R123, *Scope for control of urban runoff*[3]

- CIRIA Report R156, *Infiltration drainage: manual of good practice*[4].

Institutional barriers to the wider adoption of these techniques are being addressed by CIRIA Project RP555, "Sustainable urban runoff management"[5], which is in progress.

3.7 BETTER USE OF EXISTING STORAGE IN SEWERAGE SYSTEM

Options for making better use of existing storage in sewerage systems tend to be specific to the particular circumstances but can either be passive or active.

An example of a passive type is the addition of flow control devices in the upstream part of a system to make use of unused storage in manholes and thereby reduce peak flows farther downstream.

Active types of solution involve interaction between flow conditions and the operation of equipment such as pumps, gates and off-line storage tanks. The interaction may be achieved through the application by operations staff of written rules based on past experience, perhaps supported by analysis of the behaviour of the system using a hydraulic model. Alternatively, the operating rules may be implemented automatically by means of electronic links between the flow control equipment and sensors located at key points in the system. In the next generation of solutions, full real-time control may become an option, with a computer model forecasting flow conditions in the sewerage system and evaluating alternative strategies for operation of the control equipment; this type of option will normally tend to be applicable only on a catchment-wide basis.

The applicability of the various techniques for improving the performance of sewerage systems is discussed in CIRIA PR67, *Sewerage system management – scoping study*[6].

3.8   OVERFLOWS OR REDIRECTION OF FLOWS WITHIN SYSTEM

External overflows, bifurcations or diversions can be located at points of hydraulic overloading to remove excess flows from sewerage systems. External overflows are generally designated as combined sewer overflows (CSOs), and entail discharge of excess flow to a surface water sewer, land drain or watercourse. Diversions, together with bifurcations, are used to divert excess flows either into another part of the same system with spare capacity or into another adjacent system.

3.9   PROVISION OF STORAGE AND USE OF FLOW CONTROLS

Together with construction works to increase sewer capacity, this is the most commonly used method of solving flooding problems. Flows upstream of a critical part of the system are restricted to the capacity of the pipes by controlling and storing excess flows until the system can cope. Peak flows may be attenuated by providing purpose-built storage, usually in the form of on-line or off-line detention tanks, or by temporarily holding back surface water run-off (eg in detention ponds or in open areas such as car parks). Flow-control devices are used to control the onward flow to the downstream part of the system and/or to divert flows into storage.

3.10   CONSTRUCTION WORKS TO INCREASE SEWER CAPACITY

Together with the provision of storage, this is the most commonly used method of solving flooding problems. Existing systems are replaced or enhanced to remove the hydraulic restrictions(s) that cause the sewer flooding problems. In some cases this may be achieved by replacing an existing length of sewer by one of higher flow capacity (ie having a larger diameter or smaller hydraulic resistance). Alternatively, a length of by-pass sewer may be constructed to carry some of the flow from the existing sewer over the section where it has insufficient capacity. There is a significant risk that works to improve conditions at one location may transfer the problem farther downstream unless equivalent improvements are made all the way through the system. This possibility should be carefully investigated before new construction works are undertaken

Capital-intensive schemes to reduce flooding should not be conducted in isolation. They should be assessed on a catchment-wide basis, taking the opportunity to investigate the potential to improve receiving water quality by the reduction in the number and frequency of storm discharges. Similarly, any other operational shortcomings of the system should be addressed at the same time. This approach could improve the cost-benefit ratio of a capital-intensive scheme and thereby turn it into a "low-cost" option.

3.11   PRO-ACTIVE MAINTENANCE

This is maintenance work carried out in a planned way at key points in a sewerage system to ensure that the hydraulic capacity is not reduced by blockages or by the build-up of sediment deposits or excessive sliming in the pipes. Monitoring of the results of the work must be carried out to determine its effectiveness and, if necessary, to adjust the frequency of cleaning.

These techniques are considered in the following CIRIA publications and studies:

- CIRIA Report R141, *Design of sewers to control sediment problems*[7]
- CIRIA Report R175, *Control of infiltration to sewers*[8]
- CIRIA Project Report PR67, *Sewerage system management: scoping study*[6].
- CIRIA Project RP555, "Sustainable urban runoff management"[5]

Pro-active maintenance can sometimes be a very cost-effective way of dealing with sewer flooding problems. However, while such a solution may save a considerable amount of capital expenditure, it will usually cause some increase in operational costs. It is important that the potential benefits of pro-active maintenance are not lost because of the way in which financial controls on the capital and operational budgets of the sewerage undertakers are operated. If there are sound economic reasons for choosing this option, sewerage undertakers should explain them to Ofwat (or the relevant regulator) and supply information justifying appropriate increases in their operational budgets.

3.12 WALLS OR BUNDS

A wall or bund can be constructed around a single property, or a group of properties, to offer protection from sewer flooding, but this is only used in specific circumstances. However, bunds have been placed around manholes in foul sewerage systems as a temporary measure to minimise the extent of flooding at low points in gardens and open spaces.

3.13 PURCHASE OF PROPERTIES

This involves the sewerage undertaker purchasing a property either to remove it from a list of occupied properties affected by flooding or to change its usage so as to mitigate the effects of flooding. In some cases where flooding is confined to an occupied basement, only a change of usage for that part of the building might need to be negotiated. In all cases the proposed course of action should not be imposed on the owners of the properties but must be carried out by mutual agreement; it is only likely to be adopted in exceptional circumstances.

Procedures for selecting and implementing options

4 Sources of data on flooding problems

4.1 GENERAL

Planners, designers and operations staff require detailed information to assess, review and resolve flooding problems. Several existing sources of information can be used, as described in Sections 4.2 to 4.7.

It is important that any new information that comes to light should also be recorded and stored in the most appropriate system. Of these, probably the most useful and readily accessible will be the flooding history database kept by each sewerage undertaker. This information can then be used for statistical analysis and detailed design.

4.2 FLOODING HISTORY DATABASES

Until recently it has been difficult to obtain reliable and comprehensive data on the number and type of sewer flooding problems in the UK. Many of the sewerage undertakers inherited a wide range of uncoordinated reporting systems operated by the agent authorities carrying out sewer maintenance on their behalf. However, the Ofwat requirement for sewerage undertakers to collect data on sewer flooding incidents in England and Wales provided a major incentive for the development of more comprehensive flooding history databases. The increasing use of electronic databases and GIS systems, together with the trend for some sewerage undertakers to bring sewer maintenance work in-house, have also assisted the establishment of company-wide reporting systems.

An important element of any reporting system is an accurate knowledge of the layout of the sewer network, including the locations of private connections. Documents such as planning applications held by local authorities can also be valuable sources of information, although it should be noted that the applications may not necessarily show the systems as they were finally built. Section 24 sewers (see Chapter 2, Section 2.2) can be a particular problem because their existence and location may not be well documented, while surveying them is difficult because of their location on private land.

Collection of data is not an end in itself, and effective monitoring and analysis of the information are equally vital. Care is necessary to minimise errors in addresses and postcodes so as to prevent a single property generating several independent entries. Similarly, it is important to be able to identify from the statistics that, for example, one property has been flooded three times and not three properties each on one occasion. The location of the problem also needs to be identified accurately in terms of any reference code allocated to the pipe length concerned. A regular review of the location information should be carried out so that "hot spots" or clusters of flooding incidents are identified. Once established and operational, a flood reporting system can become a very useful tool for improving maintenance regimes and for planning new or remedial works so as to achieve the most cost-effective use of resources.

4.3   DG5 RECORDS

The DG5 register of the annual Ofwat report on levels of service provides general statistics on the numbers of flooding incidents and the numbers of properties assessed to be at risk in England and Wales (see Section 2.1). In order to be able to complete the DG5 return, each sewerage undertaker will normally have compiled a summary of the data kept in the flooding history database and/or other records. This summary may contain additional local information in a readily accessible form.

No data are available from this source for Scotland and Northern Ireland, which are not covered by DG5 reporting requirements.

A discussion on general conclusions that can be drawn from DG5 statistics, with regard to the scale of sewer flooding problems in the UK, is set out in Chapter 2.

4.4   INFORMATION FROM MAINTENANCE PERSONNEL

The maintenance teams that are called out to deal with sewer problems normally provide most of the information about flooding incidents. It is very important to make the best possible use of this primary information. Any form for recording the data, or any template for inputting it electronically into a database, needs to be practically based and unambiguous. Sketches or plans showing the location of drains and sewers can add considerably to the usefulness of the information. The data required by the form or template should be determined by the purposes for which the information is being collected (eg for DG5 statistics only, or for mapping flooding occurring both outside and inside properties). Often it may be difficult for a sewer maintenance team to determine the cause of flooding at the time of an incident, particularly if it is extensive and affects many properties. In such cases, a specialist team should carry out a follow-up investigation soon afterwards to identify the cause and enable a complete record of the incident to be made.

4.5   INFORMATION FROM OCCUPIERS OF PROPERTIES

Initial reports on flooding incidents are usually made by the occupiers of the properties who are directly affected, or inconvenienced, by the flooding. As a consequence, they often provide the basic information for the sewer maintenance team and/or the follow-up survey, see Section 4.4. This information should be recorded by the team at the time that it is received, not at a later date away from the site.

In many cases, it is advisable to consult householders around the nucleus of a flooding incident. Although they may have escaped the actual flooding, they may provide supplementary information that helps to define the true extent of a fault in the system or an operational problem.

4.6   ASSET MANAGEMENT PLANS

Sewerage undertakers prepare asset management plans (AMPs) to meet regulatory and business planning requirements. Such plans will usually address flooding problems that arise from hydraulic overloading, with a number of potential or preferred options being identified for resolution.

Often, a numerical hydraulic model will have been prepared as part of the asset management plan. If available, such a model can be used to analyse actual flooding incidents and develop solutions to these and other operational problems on a catchment-wide basis. In order to study particular flooding problems, properties at risk need to be identified as individual nodes in the model, unless there is an alternative way of identifying surcharging at intermediate locations.

Asset management plans may also give details of provisions made for carrying out pro-active and/or reactive maintenance to deal with flooding incidents arising from operational causes.

4.7 LOCAL AUTHORITY DEVELOPMENT PLANS

The asset management plans (see Section 4.6) will have been prepared against the background of the local authority's development plan and the design/planning horizons of the sewerage undertaker. If a numerical hydraulic model of the sewerage system is available, individual development proposals can be tested to ensure that the performance of the system will not be compromised. This facility also offers the opportunity to review the impacts of development plans on a catchment-wide basis.

5　Defining the nature of sewer flooding

5.1　DEFINITIONS OF FLOODING FROM SEWERS

Different definitions of flooding from sewers are used by different organisations depending on their particular objectives, needs and problems. The particular definition adopted affects the way that information on incidents and problems is selected and stored in a flooding history database (see Section 4.2).

Some databases are designed around the need to obtain the annual statistics required by Ofwat for the DG5 register (see Section 2.1). The information in this type of database is likely to be limited mainly to cases of internal flooding at occupied properties. In Scotland, which is not subject to the DG5 reporting requirements, a definition used by one Scottish water authority is: *"flooding which occurs from sewers due to rainfall"*, thereby excluding temporary problems caused by blockages, collapses and equipment failures.

Some sewerage undertakers use wider criteria for deciding what data should be recorded, and an example of a very general definition of sewer flooding is: *"The escape of sewage from a system or the inability of flow to enter a system as a result of overloading or some operational/structural fault."* A database using this type of definition would be likely to contain information on incidents affecting unoccupied buildings, open spaces and highways as well as occupied properties.

When investigating options for solving a sewer flooding problem, it is important to know what definition of flooding has been applied to any data contained in records or in a database. As a general rule, the more comprehensive the definition used, the better will be the understanding gained of the causes of the problem.

5.2　LOCATION

The effects of flooding from sewers on the general public and on physical facilities need to be considered in terms of the location in which the flooding occurs and the normal occupancy and use of that area.

Information obtained from the sources described in Chapter 4 about where the flooding occurs should be categorised as follows:

(1)　Inside a property, below ground level only　(a) occupied basement
　　　　　　　　　　　　　　　　　　　　　　　　 (b) unoccupied basement

(2)　Inside a property, above ground level　(a) occupied building
　　　　　　　　　　　　　　　　　　　　　 (b) unoccupied building

(3)　Outside a property　(a) garden
　　　　　　　　　　　　 (b) driveway or paved area

(4)　In a public highway

(5)　In an open or public area.

When deciding which problems should be targeted first, Categories 1(a) and 2(a) are likely to be assigned the highest priority, with the others varying in importance according to their degree of impact on the public.

The location of properties may also help point to possible causes of sewer flooding problems, eg:

- inner-city areas – high density of buildings, older sewerage infrastructure?

- rural areas – isolated properties, long connections to main sewers?

- new developments – difficulties with connections to existing sewerage systems?

5.3   FREQUENCY

In England and Wales, considerations as to the frequency or risk of flooding from sewers are generally based on the following categories, which correspond to Ofwat's requirements for the reporting of flooding data in the DG5 register (see Section 2.1):

(a) more than twice in 10 years

(b) more than once in 10 years but less than twice in 10 years

(c) less than once in 10 years.

It should be noted that, in the DG5 register, these categories are used only in relation to properties that are at risk of flooding due to lack of flow capacity in the sewers. In these cases, there is an implicit assumption that any flooding will be the result of heavy rainfall having approximately the same frequency of occurrence. However, when determining priorities, the frequency of all types of flooding incident should be considered. Recurring problems due to blockages, for example, may be an indicator of underlying problems in the sewerage system, and the effects are likely to be just as serious for the occupiers of properties as incidents resulting from lack of flow capacity.

In addition to DG5 records and information in flooding history databases, there may be other sources of information on the risk of flooding which should be considered, such as local knowledge and hydraulic models (see Chapter 4).

The probability of a particular flooding event can sometimes be estimated by determining from meteorological data the probability of the rainfall that produced it. However, there is often not a one-to-one relationship between the two sets of statistics; eg a one-year return period storm may not necessarily produce a one-year flood because of the effects of other factors such as duration and antecedent conditions. Also, heavy short-period thunderstorms that tend to produce the most critical cases for smaller sewerage systems can be very localised; these storms may not be picked up by the network of rain gauges operated by the Meteorological Office or be measured with sufficient accuracy by weather radars.

Due to the difficulty of assessing the frequency of flooding in a systematic way, some sewerage undertakers in England and Wales have developed and agreed with Ofwat statistical methods based on the analysis of data from their flooding history databases (see Section 4.2). As an example, the first time that a property is recorded as suffering flooding due to lack of sewer capacity, it might be assessed as being in risk category (b) above. However, if a repeat event occurred within, say, eight years, there would be enough evidence to justify assuming that the property should be in risk category (a).

Similarly, properties might be moved to a lower category if no further flooding occurred within a specified number of years.

When establishing priorities for flood prevention schemes, it is important to be aware of the way in which data on the flooding risks at individual properties have been obtained and analysed. It is also necessary to allow for the fact that records may only cover a fairly short reporting period and may not be complete as a result of some flooding incidents going unreported by the public.

5.4   EXTENT

In the design and analysis of large-scale sewerage systems it is useful to consider sewer flooding problems in terms of the total volume of sewage that could escape and/or the overall area that might be affected. However, low-cost options for preventing flooding from sewers will tend to be focused on individual properties or small groups of properties. For this reason, it is convenient in this document to describe the extent of flooding in terms of the following categories:

- individual rooms or basements
- isolated properties
- small groups of properties
- small sub-catchments.

These categories are used in Chapter 8 to demonstrate how suitable options for solving sewer-flooding problems should be selected. However, it needs to be borne in mind that some cases will have special characteristics that may cause them to bracket more than one category.

6   Identifying the cause of the problem

6.1   GENERAL

The next step in dealing with a case of sewer flooding is to determine whether or not it is caused by a hydraulic problem. The cause is considered to be hydraulic if the capacity of the system is not large enough to deal adequately with flow rates that can occur more frequently than is "acceptable". However large the capacity of a combined or surface water sewer may be,there will always be some probability that it will not be able to cope with an extreme storm event and that some surcharging or flooding will result. What constitutes an "acceptable" level of performance is usually not precisely defined because it will tend to vary with circumstances. However, as an approximate guide, a sewerage system that can handle storms with return period up to about 25 years without flooding might be considered as being "acceptable" in terms of its flow capacity.

This chapter identifies the causes of flooding from sewers that are most common in the UK. However, every sewer-flooding problem has site-specific features and sometimes there may be more than one cause.

6.2   NON-HYDRAULIC PROBLEMS

Non-hydraulic problems are generally defined as those causes of sewer flooding that are not symptoms of lack of flow capacity within the sewerage system.

The main non-hydraulic causes of flooding from sewers in the UK are:

- random blockages in pipes and intercepting traps
- pumping station and/or screening equipment failures
- burst rising mains
- high river or tide levels causing inflows to sewers
- fats and greases
- sewer collapses.

Most of the above problems can be considered as operational and system management issues. However, in some cases they may also be attributed to hydraulic characteristics.

6.3 HYDRAULIC PROBLEMS

The main hydraulic causes of flooding from sewers in the UK are:

- inadequate flow capacity in public sewers

- inadequate flow capacity in private drains

- inadequate flow capacity in Section 24 sewers (see Section 2.2)

- inadequate flow capacity in culverted watercourses

- localised downstream restrictions in public sewers

- overland flows resulting from disruption of land drainage systems

- surface water entering foul or combined sewers

- infiltration of groundwater

- properties in local low spots

- inability of drainage flows from basements to enter public sewers

- recurring blockages (due to characteristics of sewerage systems)

- siltation (due to flat sewer gradients or sewer features).

6.4 SEWERAGE SYSTEM MANAGEMENT

CIRIA Project RP560, "Sewerage system management: scoping study"[6], seeks to identify the issues that should be addressed in order to achieve efficient and effective management of sewerage systems. In this connection, the scoping study recommends that sewer flooding should be given the highest ranking in terms of priority.

The causes of flooding from sewers that can be addressed by improving the operational management of sewerage systems are listed in Figure 6.1 (produced as part of CIRIA Project RP560[6]).

6.5 SITE INVESTIGATION

The preceding sections illustrate the complexity of sewerage systems and the ways in which the many different components can interact. As a result, the problems and causes of sewer flooding at a particular location will often be site-specific. It is therefore recommended to supplement existing information about the problem (see Chapter 4) by carrying out a site investigation to identify or confirm the causes of the flooding and to aid selection of appropriate solutions.

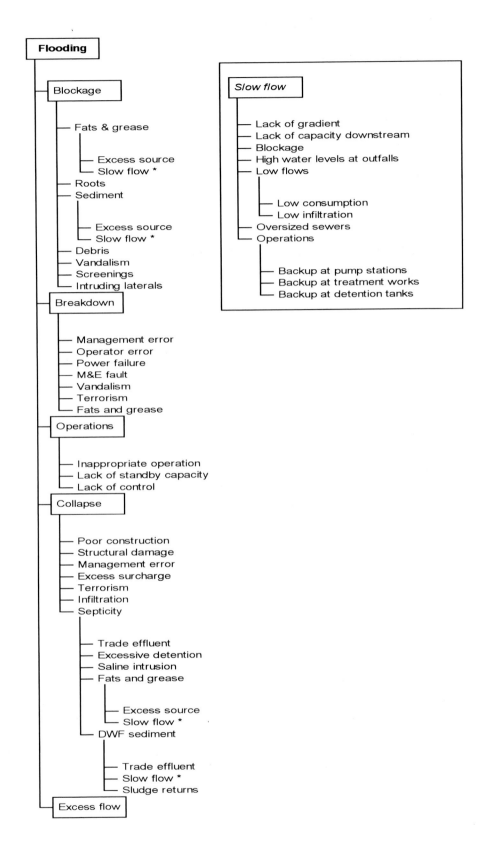

Figure 6.1 *Causes of sewer flooding that can be addressed by improved sewer system management*

7 External constraints governing choice of options

7.1 STANDARDS OF CUSTOMER SERVICE

Owners and occupiers of properties who suffer flooding from sewers are likely to consider that it represents an unacceptable standard of customer service from the sewerage undertaker, whatever may be the cause. The problems can vary in severity from temporary inconvenience (eg inability to flush WCs for short periods) to serious flooding damage and distress to the occupiers. Although foul sewage is likely to cause the worst problems, flows from surface water sewers often contain sediments and pollutants that also can leave behind unpleasant deposits and smells. Flooding incidents tend to receive prominent attention in local newspapers and can contribute adversely to the perception of a sewerage undertaker held by the general public.

In England and Wales, incidents of flooding from sewers inside properties are one of the key indicators used by Ofwat when evaluating sewerage undertakers' standards of service (see also Sections 2.1 and 7.2). Ofwat requires each sewerage undertaker to operate a Guaranteed Standards Scheme (GSS) under which customers are entitled to receive certain minimum compensation payments if specified standards of service are not met. One of the categories qualifying for payment is internal flooding of properties from sewers. In 1996–97, the number of GSS payments made in this category was 2021, with an additional 2105 payments made under companies' own supplementary schemes; the total number of flooding incidents reported to Ofwat in the same period was 4627. The amounts of compensation paid by sewerage undertakers may exceed the GSS minimum sums, and sometimes the sewerage charges may also be waived. Some companies or authorities that place a strong emphasis on customer service also take responsibility for carrying out clean-up work both outside and inside affected properties.

In the case of sewers that carry a component of surface water it is not usually possible or economic to provide sufficient flow capacity to deal with very extreme storm events. There is therefore some point beyond which it would be unreasonable to expect the sewerage undertaker to provide assurance against flooding. Surface water or combined sewers that are able to prevent flooding from storms with return periods of up to 25 years might typically be considered as providing an "acceptable" level of performance. However, no firm rules can be made because account must be taken of any particular site-specific factors (see Section 6.1).

It is worth noting that sewer-flooding incidents may go unreported by the public for several reasons. In some cases the owner or occupier of the property may consider the problem to be minor or may not wish to publicise it for fear of reducing the value of the property or of making it harder to let. There is also evidence that the proportion of incidents reported depends on how easy it is for the public to contact the sewerage undertaker through telephone help-lines, etc. From the point-of-view of obtaining more complete information about the behaviour of sewerage systems and of establishing good customer relations, it can be beneficial for the sewerage undertaker to encourage as much feedback as possible from the public. However, it is also worth noting that the public may not always know where the flooding originated and may therefore sometimes contact the wrong organisation (eg the highway authority instead of the sewerage undertaker or vice versa).

7.2 OFWAT REQUIREMENTS

The Office of Water Services (Ofwat) requires sewerage undertakers in England and Wales to provide annual information on the numbers of occupied properties that have experienced flooding from sewers and the numbers that are assessed to be at a significant risk of flooding. From these statistics Ofwat is able to identify locations where the incidence of flooding from sewers is higher than the national average. In certain cases Ofwat may require a sewerage undertaker to carry out capital works to reduce flooding problems associated with lack of flow capacity in a sewerage system. The sewerage undertaker may then be allowed to increase its charges to customers by an appropriate amount to cover some or all of the expenditure required.

Ofwat applies the DG5 statistics on flooding from sewers to achieve two purposes:

(1) To produce improvements in the levels of service provided by sewerage undertakers to their customers.

(2) To produce improvements in the infrastructure of public sewerage systems by removing existing shortcomings and by ensuring that, if necessary, their hydraulic capacities are increased to deal with changes in catchment usage.

The numbers of at-risk properties help to identify the scale of the problem and the critical locations where efforts needs to be concentrated. However, the key indicators are the numbers of flooding incidents that actually occur. As the number of years for which DG5 records are available increases, it becomes possible to analyse the data statistically and detect overall patterns and trends (although it must be recognised that there may sometimes be particular local factors that should be taken into account). Averaged over a period of years, it would be expected that the total number of properties assessed to be at risk would be between about five and 10 times the number of sewer flooding incidents occurring per year due to lack of hydraulic capacity. If this pattern is not observed, it would indicate to Ofwat either that the assessments are not giving a correct picture of the overall problem or that the reporting system is failing to record all the flooding incidents. Similarly, if the number of flooding incidents in a particular system begins to increase with time, this would suggest that changes in catchment usage have occurred, which have increased flow rates entering the system. Thus, in addition to monitoring improvements in customer service, Ofwat also uses the data on flooding incidents as an indicator of the state of the sewerage system and of its ability to deal with the flows that it experiences.

Ofwat has advised sewerage undertakers that anti-flooding devices (AFDs) are not acceptable as a means of removing properties from the DG5 register of properties that are assessed to be at risk because of hydraulic overloading of the sewers. This is partly because AFDs do not ensure a permanent drainage connection between properties and public sewers (resulting in a residual risk of a property being flooded by its own discharges), and also because AFDs do not address underlying problems of surcharging caused by lack of flow capacity. The use of AFDs does not, therefore, lead to an improvement in the public sewerage system, which is one of the objectives of the increased expenditure allowed to some sewerage undertakers.

This ruling from Ofwat does not prevent sewerage undertakers installing AFDs on their own initiative where they consider them to be appropriate. If a company uses a statistical method (see Section 5.3) for determining the number of at-risk properties, then AFDs that are effective in preventing flooding will automatically lead to properties disappearing from the DG5 register after a number of years. The position, then, is as follows: if it is essential to reduce the number of at-risk properties immediately, AFDs should not be used; if this is not the case, then the devices may be a possible option.

Pro-active maintenance can sometimes be the most cost-effective means of dealing with certain types of sewer flooding problem. In these cases the option will tend to increase operational costs while saving on capital costs. Information justifying the choice of this option should be given to Ofwat by sewerage undertakers so that can due allowance can be made in operational budgets.

7.3 PLANNING AND BUILDING REGULATIONS

7.3.1 General

Different legislation applies to planning and building works in England and Wales, Scotland and Northern Ireland, as shown in Table 7.1.

Table 7.1 *Applicable legislation in UK*

	England & Wales	Scotland	Northern Ireland
Planning	The Town and Country Planning Act 1990	Town and Country Planning (Scotland) Act 1997	Planning (General Development) Order (Northern Ireland) 1993
Building Regulations	The Building Regulations 1991	Building Standards (Scotland) Regulations 1990	Building Regulations (Northern Ireland) Order 1995

7.3.2 Planning regulations for sewer works

In general, planning laws do not cover the carrying out of works for the purposes of inspecting, repairing or renewing any sewers. Therefore planning permission would not normally be required for works connected with the prevention of flooding from sewers. However, planning permission is required for any above-ground works and structures such as pumping station control kiosks. In these cases, a formal planning application should be submitted to the planning authority (normally the local authority).

7.3.3 Planning regulations for new developments

When considering an application for planning permission for a development, the planning authority may consider drainage matters. This is relevant where an existing sewerage system is so marginal that no further development could be allowed without endangering public health. However, permission need not be refused outright and permission may be granted subject to the condition that dwellings cannot be occupied until sewer improvements have been made.

In England and Wales, sewerage undertakers do not have the status of statutory consultees in the planning process. There is therefore no legal requirement for local authorities to advise sewerage undertakers of relevant planning applications, although they may choose to do so. It is therefore recommended that sewerage undertakers should develop effective liaison with planning authorities to ensure that any developments in areas of known sewerage inadequacy, or any applications for basement conversions, are identified. In Scotland the water authorities are statutory consultees, and there would be advantages for all parties if a similar position were to apply in England and Wales.

Although new buildings require planning permission, there are exemptions for certain types of extension and for works to existing buildings. Conversion of a basement into habitable accommodation would not be considered a "development" if it affects only the interior of the building, so proposals for basement conversions are unlikely to be identified by monitoring of planning applications.

7.3.4   Building regulations

Drainage works normally are covered by building regulations (although there are exceptions such as agricultural activities). The Building Regulations in England and Wales require drainage to "be adequate". Guidance on what is considered to be adequate is given in Approved Document H[9] to the Building Regulations, which, as well as giving advice for domestic dwellings, also refers to the British Standards on the subject. For works in and around buildings, Building Regulations approval is needed. The "alternative approach" to satisfying the requirement for drainage to be adequate is to comply with recognised standards. Relevant British Standards are listed in the Bibliography.

The Building Regulations also cover sanitary conveniences and washing facilities. The main matter relating to measures for the prevention of sewer flooding is the requirement in Approved Document G1[10] to the English and Welsh Building Regulations that householders must have access to a WC connected directly to a gravity drainage system.

It is recommended that sewerage undertakers should liaise with building control departments to draw their attention to the need for effective backflow prevention in basement conversions. Also, in cases of potential basement flooding, they should seek a dispensation of the requirement in Building Regulations that householders must have access to a WC connected directly to a gravity drainage system. If this is agreed, Approved Document G1[10] allows that:

> *"a closet fitted with a macerator and pump may be connected to a small bore branch discharge pipe discharging to a discharge stack"*

provided:

> *"the macerator and pump small bore drainage system is the subject of a current European Technical Approval issued by a member body of the European Organisation for Technical Approvals, eg the British Board of Agrément, and the conditions of use are in accordance with the terms of that document."*

Building regulation control is exercised by local authorities and also by approved independent firms in certain instances.

7.4 SPECIAL FACTORS IN SCOTLAND

The three Scottish water authorities (East, North and West) are statutory water authorities in their own right, and are not regulated by Ofwat. Powers and responsibilities for carrying out sewerage works are given under the Sewerage (Scotland) Act 1968. Environmental regulation is the responsibility of the Scottish Environment Protection Agency (SEPA), which pursues polices very similar to those adopted by the Environment Agency in England and Wales.

The Scottish water authorities are carrying out asset management planning (AMP) exercises in a similar manner to those of England and Wales, and recognise sewer flooding as one of the main driving factors. As such the water authorities are in the process of consolidating existing sewer flooding reports into centralised systems to enable detailed analysis, for both AMP and operational purposes. It is anticipated that value for money and other AMP criteria will increasingly become the primary means of judging a particular sewerage scheme's need and/or effectiveness.

Culverted watercourses are believed to have contributed to a number of sewer-flooding incidents in Scotland, primarily due to capacity problems. The Flood Prevention and Land Drainage Act, which requires the unitary authorities to prepare assessments of urban watercourses, may help to differentiate the causes of flooding. Occasional flooding of basements in inner-city areas is also recognised to be a problem in Scotland.

SEPA is actively promoting source control techniques (also known as best management practices (BMPs)), as a means of improving water quality in receiving watercourses. This, in turn, is likely to have an impact on flows in sewerage systems. SEPA, in conjunction with the three Scottish water authorities, is also engaged in a programme to identify overflows and set appropriate consent standards.

7.5 SPECIAL FACTORS IN NORTHERN IRELAND

The Department of the Environment for Northern Ireland is the statutory water authority, operating through the Water Service Agency. Powers and responsibilities for carrying out sewerage works are given under the Water and Sewerage Services (Northern Ireland) Order 1973 (as amended).

Environmental regulation is the responsibility of the Environment and Heritage Service of the Department of the Environment for Northern Ireland, which pursues policies very similar to those adopted by the Environment Agency in England and Wales.

The Water Service Agency carries out asset management planning (AMP) exercises and recognises sewer flooding as a main driving factor. The Water Service Agency is in the process of producing computer models and drainage area plans for all significant catchments throughout Northern Ireland. This involves considerable liaison with the Environment and Heritage Service to ensure discharges from combined sewer overflows are reduced or eliminated where required to meet targets for improving water quality in receiving watercourses. Thus the solutions developed in drainage area plans (as part of the AMP process) involve improvements to meet criteria for both flood prevention and reduction of pollution.

In relative terms there are few properties with basements in Northern Ireland, so flooding below ground level is not considered to be as significant an issue as in some other parts of the UK.

7.6 LEGAL ASPECTS

7.6.1 Liability for installations

Sewerage undertakers have an obligation under the Water Industry Act 1991 to maintain and improve the infrastructure of the public sewerage systems and to produce improvements in the levels of service provided to their customers. This means that sewerage undertakers have to meet targets to reduce the numbers of properties at risk of flooding due to hydraulic inadequacies in the sewerage system. In England and Wales, Ofwat has legal powers to ensure that these targets are met, especially where increased expenditure has been allowed as part of periodic price reviews.

At present, sewerage undertakers are required to make payments under the Guaranteed Service Scheme (GSS) to owners of properties affected by flooding from sewers (see Section 7.1). These payments will normally represent the extent of their liability, with insurance companies bearing the costs of damage to the fabric and contents of the buildings. Some sewerage undertakers go beyond the minimum payment requirements or provide assistance with the remedial works as a means of demonstrating their commitment to customer service.

If a sewerage undertaker proposes to install a flood prevention device in a private drainage system upstream of the public sewer, some form of agreement will need to be reached with the owner of the property concerning the cost of the installation. Current practice varies between the different sewerage undertakers; some undertakers have standard written forms of agreement while others may rely on ad-hoc agreements. Legally prepared agreements are not normally necessary.

If a sewerage undertaker installs a flood prevention device that fails to operate correctly, the company may become liable for the full cost of the damage. Ofwat considers that this is a potential problem that the sewerage undertakers must accept. In order to meet Ofwat's requirements for reductions in the numbers of flooding incidents, the companies need to take positive measures. It is their responsibility to ensure that the methods they adopt are effective and do not expose them to too high a level of risk and litigation. See also Section 7.7 for details of insurance aspects.

7.6.2 Liability for maintenance

The responsibility for maintaining certain types of flood-prevention system (eg, anti-flooding devices and small pumps) may lie with the property owner or the sewerage undertaker, depending on the policy adopted by the latter. A survey carried out for an UKWIR study on anti-flooding devices[2] showed that 56% of the responding sewerage undertakers or agent authorities took responsibility for maintenance.

The extent to which sewerage undertakers will take on maintenance responsibility will increase with the size of the works. For example, it is debatable whether it should be the householder or the sewerage undertaker who is responsible for the maintenance of a small pump serving a basement. However, there can be little argument that the sewerage undertaker should maintain any length of sewer that is enlarged.

For flood prevention measures installed in a private drainage system upstream of the public sewer, some form of agreement will need to be reached with the owner of the property concerning the responsibility and cost of maintenance. As in the case of installations (see Section 7.6.1), some sewerage undertakers use standard written forms of agreement while others rely on ad-hoc (eg verbal) agreements. Legally prepared agreements are not normally necessary. To help improve customer service and to minimise flooding risk, there is a strong case for sewerage undertakers accepting responsibility for regular maintenance of devices such as anti-flooding devices and pumps that deal with all the foul drainage from properties (as opposed to pumped devices for individual appliances inside properties). Unless regular maintenance is carried out, full benefit will not be obtained from the investment made in installing some types of flood prevention system.

A concern among some sewerage undertakers is that they could remain liable for devices they have installed on private properties if the licence for operation of the public sewerage system were to be transferred to a different company at some time in the future. Definitive guidance cannot yet be given on this hypothetical situation. However, a preliminary view from Ofwat is that legislation governing a transfer of the licence would be likely to require the new operator to take over responsibility for flood-prevention devices installed by the previous operator.

7.7   INSURANCE ASPECTS

Insurance companies in the UK normally treat instances of flooding from sewers as a "natural hazard", and will therefore reimburse insured householders for the costs of repairing damage to the fabric or contents of affected properties. In special circumstances (eg extensive flooding resulting from burst mains or inadequacy of culverted watercourses), insurance companies might seek to recover their costs from the sewerage undertaker if a problem were considered to be due to negligence or a clear lack of maintenance for which the sewerage undertaker was responsible. The right of insurers to recover costs from sewerage undertakers is constrained by the case of Smeaton versus Ilford Borough Council; this case established that, unless there is negligence, the costs of damage arising from surcharging of hydraulically inadequate sewers are not recoverable.

If individual properties or localised areas have suffered repeated flooding from sewers, owners and occupiers may be asked to pay higher insurance premiums or may not be able to obtain adequate cover. In these cases, the customers affected would normally expect the sewerage undertaker to deal with the costs involved.

Due to the fact that many types of insurance claim are classed as being the result of a natural hazard, it is difficult to identify the typical level of cost associated with a sewer-flooding incident. For the cost comparisons in Appendix A4, it was assumed that the average figure would be £4000 per incident for occupied properties that suffer internal flooding and £3000 per incident for occupied basements. The average cost of claims for all types of sewer flooding, including garden flooding, is likely to be about half this figure.

8 Selecting appropriate options

8.1 DEFINING THE OBJECTIVES

The first step in dealing with a sewer-flooding problem is to identify clearly the objectives to be achieved. The following may apply either singly or in combination.

(1) **Improvement in standards of customer service**. This is likely to be a major reason for a sewerage undertaker carrying out work to reduce the number of properties at risk of being flooded from sewers. Customers who experience inconvenience, distress or damage to their properties because of sewer flooding are likely to place a high priority on the elimination of the risk. Therefore, measures that deal with this type of problem provide a clear demonstration that the sewerage undertaker is improving the standard of service to its customers. The following factors should be considered when determining the properties to be given priority:

- frequency of flooding (see Section 5.3)
- seriousness of flooding – does it cause temporary inconvenience or significant damage?
- location of at-risk properties – are there clusters that can be dealt with together?
- costs – how can the greatest benefits be obtained from available resources?

(2) **Removal of at-risk properties from the DG5 register**. This objective is closely linked to the one above but currently is relevant only to sewerage undertakers in England and Wales. Some limitations on the allowable options apply if Ofwat has agreed an increase in the sewerage undertaker's charges specifically to cover capital expenditure on reducing the number of at-risk properties. To qualify in this category, the capital expenditure must produce the reductions by means of improvements to the infrastructure of the public sewerage system (see Section 7.2). The effects of this requirement are indicated in the checklists in Sections 8.3 to 8.6.

(3) **Short-term measures**. Some at-risk properties may be located in areas where it is already planned to carry out major construction works in order to improve the hydraulic capacity of the sewerage systems (eg to cater for large-scale building developments within a catchment). The planning, detailed design and construction of such schemes can take several years, and in these circumstances it may be appropriate to provide key at-risk properties with short-term protection against flooding. A somewhat lower level of performance may be acceptable if it is known that an option will only be required to function for a limited period (within which the probability of a flood occurring may also be relatively small). Short-term measures can also help enable the remaining life of an asset to be fully utilised.

(4) **Long-term solutions**. Situations are likely to occur in which the protection of a small number of properties from sewer flooding will not justify major construction work (unless other benefits also result from the improvements). In such cases, appropriate low-cost options can provide long-term solutions that eliminate or significantly reduce the risk of flooding.

8.2   REPRESENTATIVE TYPES OF SEWER-FLOODING PROBLEM

Many problems of sewer flooding have special circumstances that can influence the choice of solution, so it is not appropriate to set down rigid rules about which option to use. The approach adopted in Sections 8.3 to 8.6 is to consider four representative types of flooding problem, ranging from individual properties to sub-catchments. For each case the possible options are described and a checklist given for identifying the key factors. In some situations the answers to the questions in a checklist may indicate clearly which option should be selected. In other situations, more than one option may be feasible and it is then necessary for the user to weigh the importance of the different factors in order to make a final selection. Some flooding problems may be intermediate in character and require more than one of the four cases to be considered.

The four representative types of sewer-flooding problem are described as follows.

Case A – Flooding in a single basement. The problem is typically caused by backflow through a low-level drainage connection between the basement and the public sewer. The rest of the property above ground level is not subject to sewer flooding and it is assumed that no other nearby property is suffering similar problems.

Case B – Flooding of a single property. Sewer flooding is occurring at ground level either inside or around the property. Again, it is assumed that no other nearby property is affected.

Case C – Flooding of properties in a street. Several adjacent properties along a street may be suffering flooding because they are situated at a low point relative to the public sewer. The number of at-risk properties might typically be between five and 20. The larger scale of the problem makes it feasible to consider a wider range of solutions than in Cases A and B.

Case D – Flooding across a sub-catchment. A larger number of properties within a sub-catchment is subject to sewer flooding, but the incidents are distributed throughout the sub-catchment rather than being concentrated in clusters.

The principal criteria for selecting suitable options to deal with these four types of flooding problem are:

- technical suitability

- cost

- reliability

- maintenance needs

- external factors such as planning and building regulations and Ofwat requirements.

Full details for Cases A to D are given in Sections 8.3 to 8.6, respectively; these sections are intended to be self-contained, so they contain some duplication of information about the possible options. The benefits obtained by preventing sewer flooding have been estimated on the basis of the likely cost of putting right the damage that would otherwise be caused. A figure of £4000 per property per flooding incident inside a property has been assumed in the cost comparisons given in Appendix A4.

8.3   CASE A: FLOODING IN A SINGLE BASEMENT

Situations where Case A is likely to be relevant include:

- conversions of cellars into occupied basements

- underground car parks and storage areas.

An example of the type of situation that applies in the case of a single basement is shown in Figure 8.1. If basements in other nearby properties are also subject to sewer flooding, Case C is likely to be more appropriate.

8.3.1   Main options

The main options for dealing with this type of problem are:

- **anti-flooding device** (AFD) – to prevent backflow from a public sewer. For details see Section 3.2 and Appendix A1.

  An AFD may have an automatic closure device (eg a hinged flap that closes when the flow direction reverses), or a powered closure device (eg an electrically operated flap linked to a water-level sensor and an alarm), or a combination of the two.

- **pumping** – to pump drainage flows from a basement into a public sewer using one or more small macerating pumps. For details see item (3) in Section 3.3 and Section A2.1 of Appendix A.

  The pumps are installed in collection tanks and use small-bore pipework, which should be taken above ground level so that drainage flow can be discharged into the sewer under all conditions. Individual sanitary appliances (eg sinks, WCs, etc) can be fitted with individual pumps (see Figure 8.1.b), or alternatively a larger unit may be installed below the floor to deal with all the drainage flows from the basement.

- **pro-active maintenance** – to prevent the build-up of deposits or blockages in the public sewer if these have been the cause of the flooding incidents. For details see Section 3.11 and Section A3.7 of Appendix A3.

- **purchase of basement** – by the sewerage undertaker, if no other options are feasible. For details see Section 3.13 and Section A3.9 of Appendix A3.

8.3.2   Costs and benefits

Data on typical costs and benefits of the above options are provided in Section A4.2 of Appendix A4.

The net present values given in Table 8.1 take account of the whole-life costs (purchase, installation, operation, maintenance and replacement) over a 15-year period, assuming

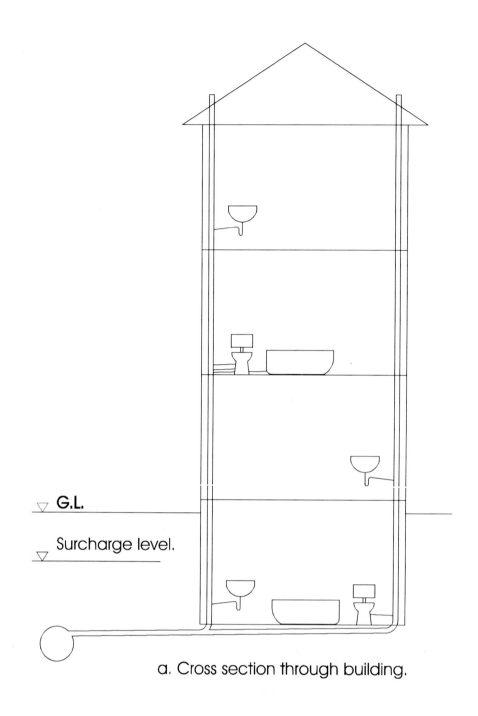

G.L.

Surcharge level.

a. Cross section through building.

Figure 8.1a   *Example of an occupied basement*

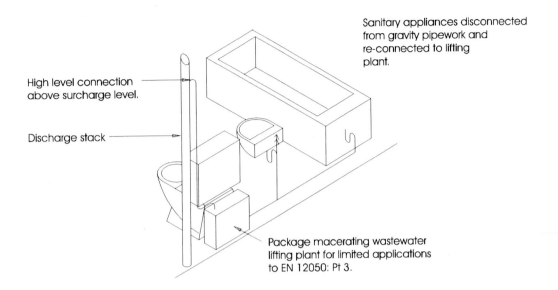

High level connection above surcharge level.

Discharge stack

Sanitary appliances disconnected from gravity pipework and re-connected to lifting plant.

Package macerating wastewater lifting plant for limited applications to EN 12050: Pt 3.

Figure 8.1b *Use of pump*

a discount rate of 7.5%. These costs are balanced by benefits calculated on the assumption that a total of three flooding incidents will be prevented during the 15 years. The figures in Table 8.1 are indicative only and are given to aid the selection of options.

Table 8.1 *Typical costs and benefits for Case A: Flooding in a single basement*

Option	Values per property	
	Initial capital cost	Net present benefit or (net present cost)
Anti-flooding device	£1k to £2k	£4k
Pumping	£1k to £2k	£4k
Pro-active maintenance	Zero	£2k
Purchase of basement	£60k	(£50k)

8.3.3　Maintenance requirements

Section 7.6.2 gives general information about forms of agreement between sewerage undertakers and owners of properties concerning maintenance responsibilities.

- **Anti-flooding device.** It is recommended that an inspection or service normally be carried out every six months. An AFD may operate very infrequently and the investment made in installing it will be wasted if the device fails to close properly when required. Upstream flooding may also be caused if an AFD becomes blocked or jammed in the closed position. Data for a limited sample of AFDs that were serviced every six months suggest that the failure rate per year due to blockage is of the order of two to four per 1000 installed.

- **Pumping.** It is recommended that an inspection or service normally be carried out every six months. Reliability will vary with the type and make of pump. Maintenance arrangements with the installer or the sewerage undertaker should be planned to ensure a rapid response in the case of failure.

- **Pro-active maintenance.** Removal of deposits and blockages from the public sewer will be the responsibility of the sewerage undertaker. Cleaning in the targeted area should initially be carried out frequently (eg every three months) until experience shows that the frequency can safely be reduced.

- **Purchase of basement.** The sewerage undertaker should incur no maintenance costs once the drainage from the basement has been disconnected.

8.3.4　Selection method

The most appropriate options for solving the flooding problem should be identified using the information above and the conclusions obtained from the answering the checklist of questions in Table 8.2.

Table 8.2 *Checklist for selection of options for Case A: Flooding in a single basement*

QUESTION	CONCLUSION IF ANSWER IS <u>YES</u>
<u>Definition of problem</u> • Is the basement unoccupied? • Is the basement a separate dwelling? • Has the basement recently been converted for occupation? • Is there seepage through the walls or floor? • Is information available on past flooding incidents and the category of risk? (eg from DG5 records, SU's database, local knowledge). • Is information on frequency of flooding lacking? • Was the flooding caused by a blockage in the private drain or the drain being undersized? • Was the flooding caused by a blockage or equipment failure in the public sewer? • Is it planned to carry out more general improvements to the sewerage system in the area? • Is overloading due to siltation or recurrent blockages in the public sewerage system?	• Problem is probably of lower priority. • Problem is probably of higher priority (as all facilities in the basement are likely to be affected). • Was the owner informed of a potential flooding problem at the planning stage? If yes, some responsibility may lie with the owner. • Is this due to high water table, burst water main or leak from adjacent private drain or public sewer? Problem may be outside scope of this document. • Assess priority on basis of average frequency of flooding: High – more than twice in 10 years Medium – more than once but less than twice in 10 years Low – less than once in 10 years. • Assess priority by further studies. • Responsibility probably lies with the property-owner. • If blockages have occurred several times, there may be a more fundamental problem in the sewer that requires investigation. • Consider providing short-term protection for the property. See also Cases C and D. • Adopt a pro-active maintenance strategy.

<u>Selection of options for problems caused by hydraulic overloading of public sewer</u>

- Is it required to provide only short-term protection for the property?

- For longer-term protection, is the objective solely to improve the level of service for the customer?

- Is removal of the property from the DG5 list of at-risk properties also a requirement? (only applicable in England and Wales).

- Is the basement floor less than 0.5 m above the soffit level of the public sewer?

- Is the public sewer likely to remain surcharged for longer than 30 minutes at a time?

- Does the private drain from the basement/cellar also carry flow from other parts of the property?

- Do the drainage flows contain faecal solids?

- Is there more than one discharge unit (eg bath, basin, shower, WC) in the basement?

- Could solving this flooding problem transfer it to another property?

- Either an AFD or pumping may be suitable, depending on other factors below.

- Pumping is likely to be a better option than an AFD for a longer-term solution, but an AFD may be satisfactory in some situations, see factors below.

- Do not use an AFD.

- Do not use an AFD.

- Use pumping. Alternatively, use an AFD with a powered closure and an alarm, and provide flow storage if basement is occupied as a separate dwelling.

- Do not use an AFD unless storage can be provided to cater for flows from the property during the expected period of sewer surcharging.

- If an AFD is selected, consider using a version with powered closure and an alarm to reduce the risk of blockage.

- If pumping is selected, decide whether to provide separate pumps for each unit or a single pump for the combined flow – see technical data in Appendix A2.

- Consider solutions in Case C.

CIRIA C506

8.4　CASE B:　FLOODING OF A SINGLE PROPERTY

Situations where Case B is likely to be relevant include:

- isolated properties (eg in non built-up areas)
- properties in localised low points relative to the public sewer
- properties with longer than normal connections to the main public sewer.

An example of the type of situation that applies in the case of a single property is shown in Figure 8.2. If several nearby properties are also subject to sewer flooding, Case C is likely to be more appropriate.

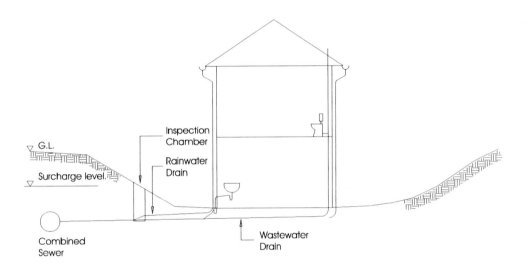

Figure 8.2　*Example of a single property*

8.4.1　Main options

The main options for dealing with this type of problem are:

- **anti-flooding device** (AFD) – to prevent backflow from a public sewer. For details see Section 3.2 and Appendix A1.

  An AFD may have an automatic closure device (eg a hinged flap that closes when the flow direction reverses), or a powered closure device (eg an electrically operated flap linked to a water-level sensor and an alarm), or a combination of the two.

- **pumping** – to pump drainage flows from a property into a public sewer using an intermediate-size pump. For details see item (2) in Section 3.3 and Section A2.1 of Appendix A. The pump will normally be installed in an inspection chamber on the private drainage system and discharge to the public sewer either under pressure or via a gravity pipe.

- **pro-active maintenance** – to prevent the build-up of deposits or blockages in the public sewer if these have been the cause of the flooding incidents. For details see Section 3.11 and Section A3.7 of Appendix A3.

- **construction of wall or bund** – to prevent overland flow from surcharged manholes, chambers or gullies draining to low points at a property. For details see Section 3.12 and Section A3.8 of Appendix A3.

- **purchase of property** – by the sewerage undertaker, if no other options are feasible. For details see Section 3.13 and Section A3.9 of Appendix A3.

8.4.2   Costs and benefits

Data on typical costs and benefits for the above options are provided in Section A4.3 of Appendix A4. The net present values given in Table 8.3 take account of the whole-life costs (purchase, installation, operation, maintenance and replacement) over a 15-year period, assuming a discount rate of 7.5%. These costs are balanced by benefits calculated on the assumption that a total of three flooding incidents will be prevented during the 15 years. The figures in Table 8.3 are indicative only and are given to aid the selection of options.

Table 8.3   *Typical costs and benefits for Case B: Flooding of a single property*

Option	Values per property	
	Initial capital cost	Net present benefit or (net present cost)
Anti-flooding device	£1k to £2k	£6k
Pumping	£3k	£4k
Pro-active maintenance	Zero	£4k
Construction of wall or bund	£1k	Not comparable with other options as only partial solution
Purchase of property	£140k	(£130k)

8.4.3   Maintenance requirements

Section 7.6.2 gives general information about forms of agreement between sewerage undertakers and owners of properties concerning maintenance responsibilities.

- **Anti-flooding device**. It is recommended that an inspection or service normally be carried out every six months. An AFD may operate very infrequently and the investment made in installing it will be wasted if the device fails to close properly when required. Upstream flooding may also be caused if an AFD becomes blocked or jammed in the closed position. Data for a limited sample of AFDs that were serviced every six months suggest that the failure rate per year due to blockage is of the order of two to four per 1000 installed.

- **Pumping.** It is recommended that an inspection or service normally be carried out every six months. Reliability will vary with the type and make of pump. Maintenance arrangements with the installer or the sewerage undertaker should be planned to ensure a rapid response in the case of failure.

- **Pro-active maintenance**. Removal of deposits and blockages from the public sewer will be the responsibility of the sewerage undertaker. Cleaning in the targeted area should initially be carried out frequently (eg every three months) until experience shows that the frequency can safely be reduced.

- **Construction of wall or bund**. Clean-up work is likely to be necessary if surface flooding occurs within the contained area.

- **Purchase of property.** No maintenance costs should be incurred once the drainage from the property has been disconnected.

8.4.4   Selection method

The most appropriate options for solving the flooding problem should be identified using the information above and the conclusions obtained from answering the checklist of questions in Table 8.4.

Table 8.4 *Checklist for selection of options for Case B: Flooding of a single property*

QUESTION	CONCLUSION IF ANSWER IS <u>YES</u>
Definition of problem • Is the flooding only external to the building and caused by overland flow from surcharged manholes, chambers or gullies? (eg garden flooding).	• Problem is probably of lower priority. Consider use of wall or bund as a temporary measure to limit flooding. Check whether the highway drainage or land drainage systems may be causing the problem.
• Is the building that is being flooded unoccupied or not designated for occupation?	• Problem is probably of lower priority. An AFD is likely to be appropriate if a solution is required.
• Is information available on past flooding incidents and the category of risk? (eg from DG5 records, SU's database, local knowledge).	• Assess priority on basis of average frequency of flooding: High – more than twice in 10 years Medium – more than once but less than twice in 10 years Low – less than once in 10 years.
• Is information on frequency of flooding lacking?	• Assess priority by further studies.
• Was the flooding caused by a blockage in the private drain or the drain being undersized?	• Responsibility probably lies with the property-owner.
• Was the flooding caused by a blockage or equipment failure in the public sewer?	• If blockages have occurred several times, there may be a more fundamental problem in the sewer that requires investigation.
• Is it planned to carry out more general improvements to the sewerage system in the area?	• Consider providing short-term protection for the property. See also Cases C and D.
• Is surcharging being caused by siltation or repeated blockages?	• Adopt a pro-active maintenance strategy.

Selection of options for problems
caused by hydraulic overloading of
public sewer

- Is it required to provide short-term protection until an improvement scheme for the sewerage system is implemented?

  - Either an AFD or pumping may be suitable, depending on other factors below.

- For longer-term protection, is the objective solely to improve the level of service for the customer?

  - Pumping is likely to be a better option than an AFD for a longer-term solution, but an AFD may be satisfactory in some situations, see factors below.

- Is it also required to remove the property from the DG5 list of at-risk properties? (only applicable in England and Wales).

  - Do not use an AFD.

- Is rainwater from the property connected to the foul drainage system?

  - The rainwater should be disconnected from the foul system if possible (eg reconnect to the surface water system, use a soakaway, connect to water butt for garden use, etc). If it is not possible to disconnect, do not use an AFD.

- Does the drainage system within the property receive flows from an adjacent property?

  - Provide the properties with individual flood-prevention devices – see also Case C.

- Is the existing storage within the private drainage system too small to contain drainage flows from the property during the period that the public sewer is likely to be surcharged?

  - For pumping, either use a larger pump with a capacity that can handle the maximum flow rate from the property, or use a smaller pump and provide some additional storage.

    For an AFD, only use a powered type with an alarm to warn occupants not to discharge flows to the drainage system – any rainwater must also be disconnected from the system upstream of the AFD.

- Could solving this flooding problem transfer it to another property?

  - Consider solutions in Case C.

CASE C: FLOODING OF PROPERTIES IN A STREET

Situations where Case C is likely to be relevant include:

- streets with a dip, resulting in shallow sewers

- streets with a steep crossfall, with properties on one side lower than street level

- streets where the upstream catchment area has been enlarged

- streets where there is a restriction on the outfall

- areas that are at a lower elevation than the rest of the catchment.

An example of the type of situation that applies is shown in Figure 8.3 where a dip part-way along the street makes a group of houses vulnerable to flooding when the sewer surcharges.

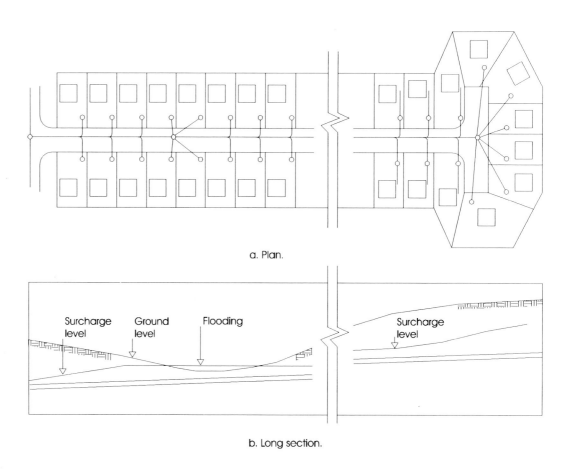

a. Plan.

b. Long section.

Figure 8.3 *Example of flooding of a street*

8.5.1   Main options

The main options for dealing with this type of problem can be grouped under three headings, as follows:

(1) Prevention of backflow

- **Anti-flooding devices** (AFDs) – to prevent backflow from a public sewer. For details see Section 3.2 and Appendix A1.

  An AFD may have an automatic closure device (eg a hinged flap that closes when the flow direction reverses), or a powered closure device (eg an electrically operated flap linked to a water-level sensor and an alarm), or a combination of the two.

  AFDs may be fitted to each individual property affected by flooding. Alternatively, the drain connections of affected properties may be disconnected from the sewer and reconnected to a gravity rider sewer. The rider sewer will then discharge to the sewer via an AFD, as illustrated in Figure 8.4. This arrangement does not require any pumping, but extra flow storage may be necessary depending on the period during which surcharging of the public sewer occurs.

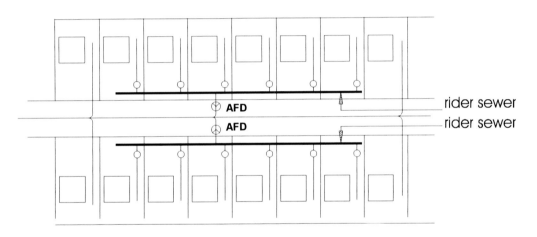

Figure 8.4   *Anti-flooding devices with a rider sewer*

- **Pumps for individual properties** – to pump drainage flows from properties into a public sewer using an intermediate-size pump at each at-risk property. For details see item (2) in Section 3.3 and Section A2.1 of Appendix A.

  This option requires only limited construction work, particularly if the existing inspection chambers are suitable for installation of the pumps. Most pumps for this kind of application are of the grinder type to allow use of small-diameter pipework, but pneumatic ejectors are also a possibility. The pumps will discharge drainage flows to the public sewer either under pressure or via gravity pipes.

(2) Disconnection of properties from gravity system

- **Pumping station** – to collect foul (and possibly surface water) flows from the affected properties by means of a gravity rider sewer connecting to a pumping station. The flow is then lifted into the public sewer above the maximum surcharge level. For details see item (1) in Section 3.3 and Section A2.1 of Appendix A2.

  A central pumping station allows use of standard equipment with proven reliability. A suitable site with public access needs to be available for the pumping station. This system is illustrated in Figure 8.5.

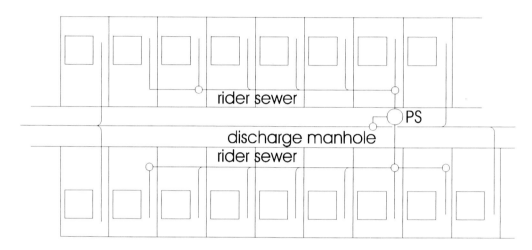

Figure 8.5 *Pumping station with rider sewers*

- **Vacuum sewerage system** – to transfer drainage flows from individual properties into a central collector station from where they are pumped into the public sewer above the maximum surcharge level. For details see Section 3.4 and Section A2.2 of Appendix A2.

  This option should be considered as an alternative to pumping if the latter would require deep rider sewers or multiple pumping stations. A suitable site with public access needs to be available for the pumping station and control kiosk.

- **Bypass sewer** – to collect drainage flows from the properties and convey them to a point on the public sewer farther downstream where discharge is not prevented by surcharging and backflow does not occur. For details see Section 3.10 and Section A3.6 of Appendix A3.

  No pumping is required, but in urban areas there may be difficulty in finding a suitable route for the new sewer. This option is shown in Figure 8.6.

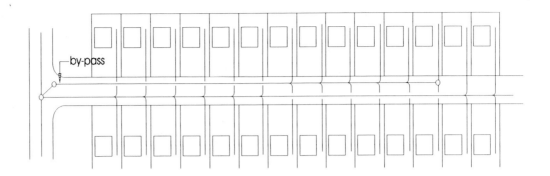

Figure 8.6 *Use of a bypass sewer*

(3) Reduction of surcharge levels

- **Structural improvements** – to remove restrictions or sources of extra head losses in the sewer that may be causing backing-up of flow at the affected properties. For details see Section 3.5 and Section A3.1 of Appendix A3.

- **Reduction/attenuation of surface water inflow** – to prevent or delay surface water entering the foul sewer in order to reduce peak flow rates and hence surcharge levels. For details see Section 3.6 and Section A3.2 of Appendix A3.

  This can be achieved by identifying malconnections of surface runoff to the foul sewer and either reconnecting them to the surface water sewer or disposing of the runoff via infiltration systems. Alternatively, the rate of inflow at surface water inlets may be reduced by means of flow-control devices.

- **Reduction of groundwater infiltration** – to reduce flow rates in the sewer by preventing groundwater leaking into it through cracked pipes or faulty joints. For details see Section 3.6 and Section A3.2 of Appendix A3.

- **Better use of existing storage in sewerage system** – to reduce surcharging in the sewer by installing flow controls upstream so as to limit the maximum flow rate in the problem area and make best use of existing upstream storage. For details see Section 3.7 and Section A3.3 of Appendix A3.

  Flow control may take the form of a vortex device or a throttle pipe, but care should be taken to provide sufficient clear passage to minimise the risk of blockage. A detailed hydraulic analysis of the system needs to be made in order to determine whether sufficient upstream storage is available. Care should be taken to avoid surcharging the upstream system to such an extent that new flooding problems occur, especially where there are properties with occupied basements.

  The effect of an upstream flow control is illustrated in Figure 8.7.

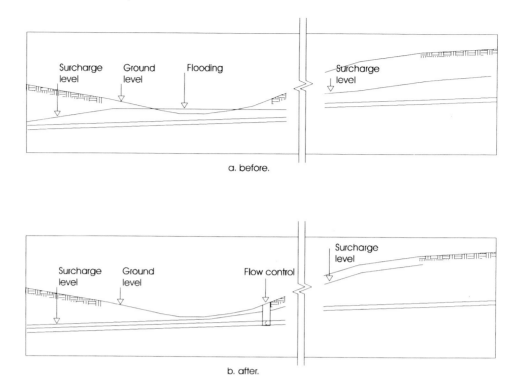

Figure 8.7   *Effect of installing upstream flow control*

- **Diversion of flow** – to reduce surcharging of the sewer by diverting part of the flow upstream of the affected area into another part of the sewerage system that has some spare capacity. For details see Section 3.8 and Section A3.4 of Appendix A3.

  A detailed hydraulic analysis of the system needs to be made in order to determine whether sufficient flow capacity exists in other lengths of sewer.

- **Combined sewer overflow (CSO)** – to reduce surcharging of the sewer by diverting part of the flow upstream of the affected area to a watercourse. For details see Section 3.8 and Section A3.4 of Appendix A3.

  Agreement will need to be obtained from the relevant environmental regulator. It is likely that a detailed hydraulic analysis of the system will need to be made in order to determine the frequency, volume and polluting effects of overflows. Studies of the receiving water may also be required.

- **Provision of storage and use of flow controls** – to reduce peak flow rates in the sewer by using flow controls to hold wastewater temporarily in upstream storage. For details see Section 3.9 and Section A3.5.

  Below-ground storage can take the form of on-line tanks, off-line tanks, enlarged sections of sewers, or oversized manholes. The filling and emptying of tanks may be controlled by flow controls such as vortex devices or throttle pipes. The tanks should be designed, so far as possible, to be self-cleansing to minimise maintenance requirements.

- **Construction works to increase sewer capacity** – to increase the flow capacity of the sewer and lower surcharge levels sufficiently to prevent flooding at the affected properties. This is usually achieved by replacing a length of existing sewer with a larger one or by constructing a parallel length of relief sewer. For details see Section 3.10 and Section A3.6 of Appendix A3.

- **Pro-active maintenance** – to remove downstream blockages and sediment deposits that may be causing backing-up of flow at the affected properties. For details see Section 3.11 and Section A3.7 of Appendix A3.

8.5.2 Costs and benefits

Data on typical costs and benefits for each of the options described above are provided in Section A4.4 of Appendix A4. The net present values given in Table 8.5 take account of the whole-life costs (purchase, installation, operation, maintenance and replacement) over a 15-year period, assuming a discount rate of 7.5%. These costs are balanced by benefits calculated on the assumption that a total of three flooding events affecting the street of properties will be prevented during the 15 years. The values in Table 8.5 are indicative only and are given to aid the selection of options.

8.5.3 Maintenance requirements

Section 7.6.2 gives general information about forms of agreement between sewerage undertakers and owners of properties concerning maintenance responsibilities.

- **Anti-flooding devices**. It is recommended that an inspection or service should be carried out every six months. An AFD may operate very infrequently and the investment made in installing it will be wasted if the device fails to close properly when required. Upstream flooding may also be caused if an AFD becomes blocked or jammed in the closed position. Data for a limited sample of AFDs that were serviced every six months suggest that the failure rate per year due to blockage is of the order of two to four per 1000 installed.

- **Pumps**. It is recommended that an inspection or service should normally be carried out every six months. Reliability will vary with the type and make of pump. Maintenance arrangements with the installer or the sewerage undertaker should be planned to ensure a rapid response in the case of failure.

- **Vacuum sewerage systems**. It is recommended that a telemetry system should be installed to indicate any failure in the system, eg an interface valve not sealing. A maintenance contract should be in place to ensure that problems can be remedied quickly and that spare components are kept in stock. The pumps should be inspected or serviced every six months.

Table 8.5 *Typical costs and benefits for Case C: Flooding of properties in a street*

Option	Values per property	
	Initial capital cost	Net present benefit or (net present cost)
Anti-flooding devices for individual properties	£1k	£6k
Anti-flooding device with rider sewer	£3k	£6k
Pumps for individual properties	£2k	£4k
Pumping station with rider sewer	£2k	£6k
Vacuum sewerage system	Site specific	Site specific
Bypass sewer	£4k	£3k
Structural improvements	£0.2k	£7k
Reduction of surface water inflow	£2k	£5k
Reduction of groundwater infiltration	£2k	£6k
Better use of existing storage in sewerage system	£0.5k	£7k
Diversion of flow	£2k	£5k
Provision of storage and use of flow controls	£2k	£5k
Construction works to increase sewer capacity	£5k	£2k
Pro-active maintenance	£0.1k	£7k

- **Reduction of surface water inflow**. Malconnections tend to be made at random times. Therefore, where flooding problems have been solved by reduction of surface water, routine surveying should be undertaken periodically to identify any new connections added since remedial works were carried out.

- **Upstream flow control**. Depending upon the type and size of flow control used, this is a potential point of blockage and the device should be regularly inspected and cleaned if necessary. It is recommended that initially this should be carried out with frequent visits, say every three months, until experience indicates that the frequency may be reduced.

- **Reduction of ground water infiltration**. Sealing of the system against groundwater ingress may alter the water table. This could result in previously watertight sections of pipework and chambers subsequently developing leaks. Therefore reduction of groundwater tends to require continual effort, and an inspection is recommended after the initial sealing works, when groundwater levels are high.

- **Overflows**. A properly designed overflow should be screened to prevent gross pollution being discharged from the sewerage system. Maintenance will include inspection and cleaning of screens after each discharge. Failure to keep the screens clean will result in odour problems and the likelihood of the overflow failing to work due to blockage.

- **Provision of storage and use of flow controls**. Some types of storage tank may require emptying or cleaning after each storm event. Where storage takes the form of an enlarged section of sewer, siltation could be a problem and regular de-silting may be required. Initially the cleaning should be carried out frequently (eg every three months) and later reduced if experience indicates that it is safe to do so.

  Depending upon the type and size of flow control used, this is a potential point of blockage and initially should be regularly inspected and cleaned if necessary. It is recommended that frequent visits should initially be made (eg every three months) until experience indicates that the frequency may safely be reduced.

- **Pro-active maintenance**. Removal of deposits and blockages from the public sewer will be the responsibility of the sewerage undertaker. Cleaning in the targeted area should initially be carried out frequently (eg every three months until experience shows that the frequency can safely be reduced).

8.5.4   Selection method

The most appropriate options for solving the flooding problem should be identified using the information above and the conclusions obtained from answering the questions in Table 8.6.

In order to choose the most appropriate option, it is important that the cause of the flooding be established and that the response of the sewerage system be determined.

Table 8.6 *Checklist for selection of options for Case C: Flooding of properties in a street*

QUESTION	CONCLUSION IF ANSWER IS <u>YES</u>
Definition of problem	
• Is the flooding a result of overland surface water flows, overtopping of a watercourse or springs?	• Check whether faulty or inadequate land drainage systems may be causing the problem.
• Is the flooding only external to buildings and caused by overland flow from surcharged manholes, chambers or gullies (eg garden flooding)?	• Problem is probably of lower priority. Consider use of wall or bund as a temporary measure to limit flooding. Check whether highway or land drainage systems may be causing the problem.
• Are the properties being flooded unoccupied or not designated for occupation?	• Problem is probably of lower priority. AFDs are likely to be appropriate if a solution is required.
• Is information available on past flooding incidents and the category of risk? (eg DG5 records, SU's data base, local knowledge)	• Assess priority on basis of average frequency of flooding: High – more than twice in 10 years Medium – more than once but less than twice in 10 years Low – less than once in 10 years.
• Is information on the frequency of flooding lacking?	• Assess priority by further studies.
• Was the flooding caused by a blockage in a private drain or by the drains being undersized?	• Responsibility probably lies with one or more of the property-owners.
• Was the flooding caused by a blockage or equipment failure in the public sewer?	• If blockages have occurred several times, there may be a more fundamental problem in the sewer that requires investigation.
• Is it planned to carry out more general improvements to the sewerage system in the area?	• Consider providing short-term protection for the property. See also Case D.
• Is surcharging being caused by siltation or repeated blockages?	• Adopt pro-active maintenance strategy.

<u>Selection of options for problems caused by hydraulic overloading of public sewer</u>

• Is there evidence that surcharging is being caused by a local restriction in the sewerage system?	• Carry out a survey to locate the restriction and implement improvement works.
• Is it required to provide short-term protection until an improvement scheme for the sewerage system is implemented?	• Either AFDs, pumping of flows from individual properties or a CSO may be suitable, depending upon other factors below.
• For longer-term protection, is the objective solely to improve the level of service for the customers?	• Pumping of combined properties is likely to be a better option than AFDs for a longer-term solution, but AFDs may be satisfactory in some situations. Other options are: – better use of existing storage – provision of storage and use of flow controls – reduction of inflows – increase in sewer capacity.
• Is it also required to remove the properties from the DG5 list of at-risk properties? (only applicable to England and Wales).	• Do not use AFDs.
• Are ground conditions difficult for laying pipes or are the at-risk properties widely spaced?	• Consider use of a vacuum sewerage system.
• Is rainwater from the properties connected to the foul drainage system?	• Rainwater should be disconnected from the foul system if possible (eg reconnect to a surface water system, use a soakaway, connect to water butts for garden use, etc). If it is not possible to disconnect, do not use a vacuum sewerage system. If AFDs are used, sufficient storage must be provided.
• Does the drainage system of any property receive flows from another property?	• Where use of multiple AFDs or pumps is under consideration, consider protecting each property separately.

• Is the existing storage within the private drainage systems too small to contain drainage flows from the properties during the period that the public sewer is likely to be surcharged?	• For AFDs, use a powered type with an alarm to warn occupants not to discharge flows to the drainage system; also, any rainwater must be disconnected from the system upstream of the AFD. Do not use automatic-type AFDs without increasing storage.
• Is there scope for reducing the level of surcharge by controlling upstream flows?	• Solve problem by controlling flows and providing supplementary storage where necessary.
• Could solving this flooding problem by AFD or pumping have the effect of transferring it to other properties?	• Do not use AFDs or pumping. Select another option
• Could a solution based on increasing sewer capacity (eg sewer enlargement, bypass sewer, pro-active maintenance or minor structural improvements) have the effect of transferring the flooding problem to another area?	• Solve the problem by reducing flows.

CASE D: FLOODING OF PROPERTIES ACROSS A SUB-CATCHMENT

Situations where Case D is likely to be relevant include:

- areas which are at a lower elevation than the rest of the catchment

- particular areas where a greater than average incidence of flooding has been identified

- areas where general surcharging needs to be reduced or prevented.

It is assumed that the at-risk properties are not close to each other nor in small discrete areas. If several nearby properties are subject to sewer flooding, Case C is likely to be more appropriate.

8.6.1 Main options

The main options for dealing with this type of problem are:

- **anti-flooding devices** (AFDs) – to prevent backflow into individual properties from public sewers. For details see Section 3.2 and Appendix A1.

  An AFD may have an automatic closure device (eg a hinged flap that closes when the flow direction reverses), or a powered closure device (eg an electrically operated flap linked to a water-level sensor and an alarm), or a combination of the two.

  Individual properties can be dealt with in the same way as in Case B in Section 8.4. However, assuming a reliability of the order of 95% for AFDs, some flooding incidents are still likely to occur if large numbers of devices are installed in a sub-catchment that is prone to sewer flooding. However, AFDs can be a useful short-term measure because their use can produce a worthwhile improvement in the level of service provided to owners and occupiers of at-risk properties and can help to demonstrate that the sewerage undertaker is taking action to deal with the problem.

- **pumps for individual properties** – to pump drainage flows from properties into a public sewer using an intermediate-size pump at each at-risk property. For details see item (2) in Section 3.3 and Section A2.1 of Appendix A.

  Individual properties can be dealt with in the same way as in Case B in Section 8.4. The use of a large number of separate pumps increases the chance that a few of the pumps may be unserviceable when a major flood event occurs in a sub-catchment prone to sewer flooding. However, the installation of pumps can still provide a significant improvement in the overall level of service provided for owners and occupiers of at-risk properties.

- **better use of existing storage in sewerage system** – to reduce surcharging in the sewers by installing flow controls upstream so as to limit the maximum flow rate in the problem area and make best use of existing upstream storage. For details see Section 3.7 and Section A3.3 of Appendix A3.

  Flow control may take the form of a vortex device or a throttle pipe, but care should be taken to provide sufficient clear passage to minimise the risk of blockage. A detailed hydraulic analysis of the system needs to be made in order to determine whether sufficient upstream storage is available. Care should be taken to avoid surcharging the upstream system to such an extent that new flooding problems occur, especially where there are properties with occupied basements.

- **combined sewer overflow (CSO)** – to reduce surcharging of the sewer by diverting part of the flow upstream of the affected area to a watercourse. For details see Section 3.8 and Section A3.4 of Appendix A3.

Flooding often results in sewage being discharged to watercourses, involving considerable nuisance to properties in its path. An overflow will not worsen the situation, but will prevent the nuisance and distress of overland flows. Therefore construction of an overflow or rationalisation of overflows, particularly on a combined sewer, may be acceptable as an interim measure, subject to agreement from the relevant environmental regulator. It is likely that a detailed hydraulic analysis of the sewerage system will need to be made in order to determine the frequency, volume and polluting effects of overflows. Studies of the receiving water may also be required.

- **provision of storage and use of flow controls** – to reduce peak flow rates in the sewer by using flow controls to hold wastewater temporarily in upstream storage. For details see Section 3.9 and Section A3.5.

Below-ground storage can take the form of on-line tanks, off-line tanks, enlarged sections of sewers, or oversized manholes. The filling and emptying of tanks may be controlled by flow controls such as vortex devices or throttle pipes. The tanks should be designed, as far as possible, to be self-cleansing to minimise maintenance requirements.

An advantage of this type of solution is that a staged approach can be adopted, with immediate benefit accruing to downstream areas of the catchment following the installation of each of the upstream controls.

- **construction works to increase sewer capacity** – to increase the flow capacity of the sewer and lower surcharge levels sufficiently to prevent flooding at the affected properties. This is usually achieved by replacing a length of existing sewer with a larger one or by constructing a parallel length of relief sewer. For details see Section 3.10 and Section A3.6 of Appendix A3.

This is the traditional approach to dealing with sewer flooding problems. Although generally effective at preventing flooding in one area, often the problem is moved rather than solved. Therefore, the implications across the catchment as a whole need to be investigated before carrying out upgrading works.

Major sewer construction work tends to be expensive and also disruptive for the public, though modern no-dig methods can reduce the amount of disruption. The advantage of new construction works is that, in addition to solving current problems, allowance can be made for future catchment developments and improved performance criteria.

- **pro-active maintenance** – to remove downstream blockages and sediment deposits that may be causing backing-up of flow at the affected properties. For details see Section 3.11 and Section A3.7 of Appendix A3.

8.6.2 Costs and benefits

Data on typical costs and benefits for each of the options described above are provided in Section A4.5 of Appendix A.4. The net present values given in Table 8.7 take account of the whole-life costs (purchase, installation, operation, maintenance and replacement) over a 15-year period, assuming a discount rate of 7.5%. These costs are balanced by benefits calculated on the assumption that a total of three flooding events in the sub-catchment will be prevented during the 15 years. The figures in Table 8.7 are indicative only and are given to aid the selection of options.

Table 8.7   *Typical costs and benefits for Case D: Flooding of properties across a sub-catchment*

Option	Values per property	
	Initial capital cost	Net present benefit or (net present cost)
Anti-flooding devices for individual properties	£1k to £2k	£6k
Pumps for individual properties	£2k to £3k	£4k
Better use of existing storage in sewerage system	£6k	£1k
Combined sewer overflow	£4k	£3k
Provision of storage and use of flow controls	£10k	(£3k)
Construction works to increase sewer capacity	£40k	(£33k)
Pro-active maintenance	£0.5k	£5k

8.6.3 Maintenance requirements

Section 7.6.2 gives general information about forms of agreement between sewerage undertakers and owners of properties concerning maintenance responsibilities.

- **Anti-flooding devices.** It is recommended that an inspection or service normally be carried out every six months. An AFD may operate very infrequently and the investment made in installing it will be wasted if the device fails to close properly when required. Upstream flooding may also be caused if an AFD becomes blocked or jammed in the closed position. Data for a limited sample of AFDs that were serviced every six months suggest that the failure rate per year due to blockage is of the order of two to four per 1000 installed.

- **Pumps for individual properties**. It is recommended that an inspection or service normally be carried out every six moths. Reliability will vary with the type and make of pump. Maintenance arrangements with the installer or the sewerage undertaker should be planned to ensure a rapid response in the case of failure.

- **Better use of existing storage in sewerage system**. Maintenance will generally be carried out as part of the sewerage undertaker's standard operational procedures. The cost implications associated with the maintenance of flow controls have yet to be fully defined.

- **Combined sewer overflow**. A properly designed overflow should have screens to prevent gross pollution being discharged from the sewerage system. Maintenance will ensure that the overflow does not fail to operate due to blockage.

- **Provision of storage and use of flow controls.** Some types of storage tank may require emptying or cleaning after each storm event. Where storage takes the form of an enlarged section of sewer, siltation could be a problem and regular de-silting may be required; initially the cleaning should be carried out frequently (eg every three months) and later reduced if experience indicates that it is safe to do so.

  Depending upon the type and size of flow control used, this is a potential point of blockage and initially should be regularly inspected and cleaned if necessary. It is recommended that frequent visits should initially be made (eg every three months) until experience indicates that the frequency may safely be reduced.

- **Construction works to increase sewer capacity**. Maintenance will generally be carried out as part of the sewerage undertaker's standard operational procedures.

- **Pro-active maintenance**. Removal of deposits and blockages from the public sewer will be the responsibility of the sewerage undertaker. Cleaning should initially be carried out frequently (eg every three months) until experience shows that the frequency can safely be reduced.

8.6.4   Selection method

The most appropriate options for solving the flooding problems should be identified using the information above and the conclusions obtained from answering the checklist of questions in Table 8.8.

In order to choose the most appropriate option, it is important that the cause of the flooding be established and that the response of the sewerage system be understood.

Table 8.8 *Checklist for selection of options for Case D:*
Flooding of properties across a sub-catchment

QUESTION	CONCLUSION IF ANSWER IS <u>YES</u>
Definition of problem	
• Is the flooding only external and caused by overland flow from surcharged manholes, chambers or gullies? (eg garden flooding).	• Problem is probably of lower priority. Check whether highway drainage or land drainage systems may be causing the problem.
• Is information available on past flooding incidents and the category of risk? (eg. DG5 records, SU's data base, local knowledge).	• Assess priority on basis of average frequency of flooding: High – more than twice in 10 years Medium – more than once but less than twice in 10 years Low – less than once in 10 years
• Is information on the frequency of flooding lacking?	• Assess priority by further studies.
• Was the flooding caused by a blockage or equipment failure in the public sewer?	• If blockages have occurred several times, there may be a more fundamental problem in the sewer that requires investigation.
• Is it planned to carry out more general improvements to the sewerage system in the area?	• Consider providing short-term protection for the properties.
• Is a hydraulic model of the system already in existence?	• Establish that the model is verified. If so, use it to simulate the reported system deficiencies and then model and verify proposed solutions.
Selection of options for problems caused by hydraulic overloading of public sewer	
• Is it required to provide short-term protection until an improvement scheme for the sewerage system is implemented?	• Either individual AFDs or pumps may be suitable, depending on other factors below. Also an interim CSO may be a possibility.

• For longer-term protection, is the objective solely to improve the levels of service for the customers?	• Pumps are likely to be a better option than AFDs for a longer-term solution, but AFDs may be satisfactory in some situations. For these two options, see also Case C and Table 8.6.
	
	Other possible options are:
	
	  – better use of existing storage
	  – provision of storage and use of flow controls
	  – reduction of inflows
	  – increase of sewer capacity.

• Is it also required to remove the properties from the DG5 list of at-risk properties? (only applicable in England and Wales).	• Do not use AFDs.
• Is there scope for solving the problem by reducing the level of surcharge by controlling upstream flows?	• Solve problem by controlling flows and providing supplementary storage where necessary.
• Could a solution based on increasing sewer capacity (eg sewer enlargement, bypass sewer, pro-active maintenance or minor structural improvements) have the effect of transferring the flooding problem to another area?	• Solve the problem by reducing flows. Also consider individual and/or integrated solutions on a catchment-wide basis using hydraulic models and drainage area studies.

9 Implementing the selected solution

9.1 GENERAL

Implementation of a scheme for preventing flooding from sewers will normally follow the same process as for other drainage or sewerage projects.

The main stages that should be carried out when implementing a scheme are illustrated in Figure 9.1. The importance of consultation at all stages cannot be over-emphasised if the scheme is to be successful.

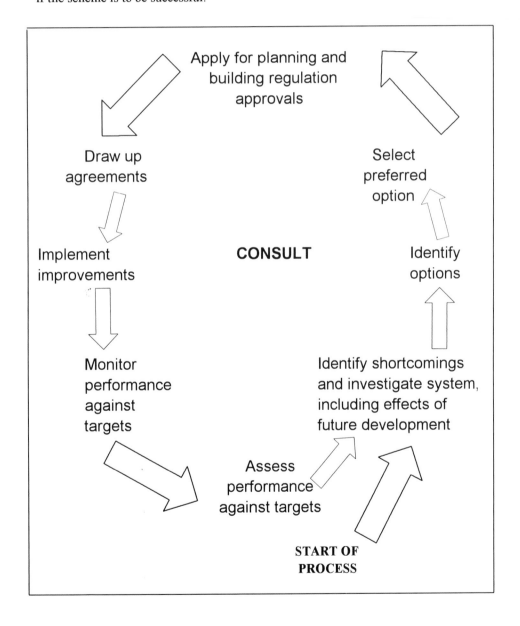

Figure 9.1 *Implementation*

Consultation should continue throughout all the stages of a scheme in order to address the following issues:

- correct definition of the cause and extent of the problem
- identification of options
- acceptability of proposed solution
- implications of proposed solution
- costs and benefits of proposed solutions
- maintenance responsibilities and actions
- public relations during construction works
- effectiveness of the implemented scheme.

Consultees may include:

- sewerage undertaker (if it is not the organisation proposing the change)
- Ofwat
- environmental authority (EA, SEPA or DOE(NI))
- policy-making departments of organisation proposing change
- affected public
- general public
- planners
- building controls departments
- maintenance operatives
- legal department of organisation proposing changes
- suppliers and installers.

9.2   DEALING WITH THE PUBLIC

Flooding, and foul sewage flooding in particular, is an emotive issue. Therefore it is important that the public, and particularly those directly affected, should be kept informed of actions that are being taken, even if the action is to apply for a financial budget to carry out the next stage of the project.

Public acceptance of works and the resulting inconvenience will be much greater if the sewerage undertaker keeps them informed and allows them to participate in the decision-making process. This will speed up the works, minimise the risk of confrontation and adverse publicity, and lead to lower overall cost.

As prevention of flooding is chiefly a customer service criterion, consultation will allow customer expectations to be determined and best met. Where there is a gap between expectation and what can be practically achieved, the problems can be explored and ways found to reach a mutually agreeable solution.

Construction work may directly affect properties and appropriate measures should be taken to protect them.

9.3   LEGAL AGREEMENTS

Legal agreements are discussed in Section 7.6. These include legal agreements to carry out the work in private premises and for their subsequent maintenance

It is recommended that a simple written agreement should be drawn up in order to avoid difficulties of misconception, but normally it will not need to be a formal legal document. The agreement should record:

Installation

- why the works are needed

- what the works comprise

- expected performance of the works

- who will pay for the works

- compensation, if any, for inconvenience

- levels of service anticipated (eg design storm return period and whether it is an interim or permanent measure)

- when the works will be carried out

- responsibility for any damage during the works.

Maintenance

- who will be responsible for maintenance

- frequency of maintenance visits, including timings

- operating instructions

- emergency instructions.

General

- contact point

- request for feedback.

9.4   MONITORING PERFORMANCE

It is good practice to monitor the actual performance of any scheme against its predicted performance, in order to:

- justify the spending on the scheme (to satisfy the need for accountability)

- identify any shortcomings that need to be addressed to fulfil the desired level of service

- allow policy and design parameters to be adjusted in the light of experience (eg by standardising on the most successful devices or options)

- improve public relations.

10 References

1. OFWAT. *1996–97 Report on levels of service for the water industry in England and Wales.* Office of Water Services. 1997.

2. MAY R W P. *Effectiveness of anti-flooding devices in sewers and drains.* UKWIR Report (to be published), 1997.

3. CIRIA. *Scope for control of urban runoff, Volume 1: Overview.* Report R123, 1992.

4. CIRIA. *Infiltration drainage – manual of good practice.* Report R156, 1996.

5. CIRIA. "Sustainable urban runoff management". Project RP555. In preparation.

6. CIRIA. *Sewerage system management – scoping study.* Project Report PR67. In preparation, 1998.

7. CIRIA. *Design of sewers to control sediment problems.* Report R141, 1996.

8. CIRIA. *Control of infiltration to sewers.* Report R175, 1997.

9. DEPARTMENT OF THE ENVIRONMENT AND THE WELSH OFFICE. *The Building Regulations 1991.* Approved Document H "Drainage and waste disposal". Amended 1992.

10. DEPARTMENT OF THE ENVIRONMENT AND THE WELSH OFFICE. *The Building Regulations 1991.* Approved Document G "Hygiene", 1992 edition.

11. WATER SERVICES ASSOCIATION. *Sewers for Adoption – a design and construction guide for developers.* 4th edition, 1995.

11 Bibliography

British and European Standards

(Pr EN denotes Provisional draft European Standard)

BS 5572   Code of practice for sanitary pipework. British Standards Institution. 1994.

BS 6367   Code of practice for drainage of roofs and paved areas. British Standards Institution. 1983.

BS 8005   Sewerage (partially replaced by BS EN 752). British Standards Institution. 1987.

BS 8301   Code of practice for building drainage (partially replaced by BS EN 752). British Standards Institution. 1985.

BS EN 752   Drain and sewer systems outside buildings (superseding BS 8005 and BS 8301). British Standards Institution. 1995, 1996.

BS EN 1091   Vacuum sewerage systems outside buildings. British Standards Institution. 1996.

BS EN 1671   Pressure sewerage systems outside buildings. British Standards Institution. 1997.

Pr EN 12050   Effluent lifting plants for buildings and sites.

Pr EN 12056   Gravity drainage systems inside buildings. Part 4: Effluent lifting plants, layout and calculation.

Pr EN   Anti-flooding devices for buildings. Part 1: Requirements; Part 2: Test methods.

Pr EN   Vacuum sewerage systems inside buildings.

Building Research Establishment

GRG 11   Repairing flood damage: Parts 1 to 4. 1997.

Appendices

Detailed technical data on options

Appendix A1 Technical data on anti-flooding devices

A1.1 DESCRIPTION

An anti-flooding device (AFD) is an in-line device designed for installation in a gravity sewer or drain to prevent backflow. It needs to cause a minimum of extra head loss when open and be resistant to blockage. The AFD may contain one or more closure devices, which can include flap gates, gate valves or ball valves. The majority of anti-flooding devices that are available use flap gates.

Other types of backflow preventer include tide flaps and check valves used with pumps. However, in general, these are not suitable for use in gravity systems either because they produce too high a head loss or do not seal reliably when there is material such as grit, rag or faecal solids in the flow. These types are not considered further here.

A1.2 EUROPEAN STANDARD (SEE BIBLIOGRAPHY)

A draft European product standard covering anti-flooding devices has been prepared by CEN Technical Committee TC 165/WG 4/AHG 5. If the Standard is finally approved by European national votes, it could come into force before the end of 1999.

Part 1 of the draft Standard defines technical requirements for the following classes of anti-flooding device:

Type 1   for use in horizontal pipes having an automatic closure device and an emergency closure device that can be locked shut; the two devices may be separate or combined into one.

Type 2   similar to Type 1 but having two automatic closure devices and an emergency closure device (which may be combined with one of the automatic devices).

Type 3   for use in horizontal pipes, with an automatic closure device actuated by external energy and a separate emergency closure device.

Type 4   similar to Type 1 but for use with waste fittings or floor gullies.

Type 5   similar to Type 2 but for use with waste fittings or floor gullies.

The draft Standard does not specify what form the automatic and emergency closure devices within an AFD should take, but the most common are circular flap gates (sometimes with float-assisted closure), ball valves, vertical slide gates and sections of flexible pipe that can be compressed or rotated to prevent flow.

Part 2 of the draft Standard specifies test methods to be used for checking that the material properties of the AFDs are satisfactory and that they can resist blockage by debris in the flow. The flow tests use a liquid mixture consisting of water and a variety of solid particles to simulate the characteristics of sewage. A separate test is also required to simulate blockage by rags trapped in the AFD. Limits on the amounts of backflow that can be allowed in the tests due to leakage past the closure devices are specified in the Standard.

A1.3 TYPES OF APPLICATION

Anti-flooding devices are normally, but not always, installed in private drains upstream of the connections with the public sewers. The devices are typically between 0.5 m and 1 m long, and the EN Types 1, 2 and 3 (see Section A1.2) are usually mounted in-line inside an inspection chamber or manhole to allow access for maintenance. The AFDs corresponding to Types 4 and 5 in the EN are commonly manufactured as integral parts of floor gullies or waste fittings.

If an anti-flooding device closes due to backflow, it temporarily disconnects the property from the public sewerage system. If appliances within a property continue to be used, there is a danger that the property may still be flooded by its own drainage discharges. When investigating the possibility of an installation, it is therefore necessary to consider the amount of storage within the chambers and pipes of the private drainage system in relation to the time that the sewer could be surcharged and the volume of discharge that could be generated in that time. A method of reducing the risk of flooding when an AFD closes is to use a Type 3 device that is operated by external energy and that incorporates an alarm to warn the householder that the sewer has become surcharged.

When evaluating solutions for property flooding, some sewerage undertakers will install an anti-flooding device only if some or all of the following criteria are satisfied:

- the sewer flooding only occurs below ground

- the AFD will not serve more than property

- any surface water flows (eg from roofs or patios) entering the private drainage system upstream of the AFD are excluded or diverted

- the AFD should not simply transfer the flooding problem to another property.

Ofwat has ruled that installation of an anti-flooding device will not be considered as removing a property from the DG5 register of at-risk properties. However, this type of device can be installed quickly and relatively cheaply, and in many cases will provide improved protection for at-risk properties.

A1.4 EXTENT OF USAGE

Information on the numbers of anti-flooding devices installed in the UK was obtained as part of a study[2] carried out for UK Water Industry Research Limited (UKWIR) in 1996. Based on a survey of sewerage undertakers, it was estimated that the national total was at least 4000 AFDs; the lack of reliable and centralised maintenance records makes it likely that the true figure is considerably higher. Evidence for this was provided by a parallel survey of manufacturers, which showed that at least 1500 new anti-flooding devices were sold in the UK in 1996.

A1.5   COSTS

The cost of a Type 1 or Type 2 anti-flooding device (see Section A1.2) manufactured in plastic is typically in the range £200 to £400. The traditional types of float-operated cast-iron device are larger and more expensive (eg £900 for a 150 mm-diameter valve). Type 3 AFDs with a powered closure device and an alarm cost around £1500. The smaller plastic AFDs can often be installed in existing chambers at a cost of the order of £250. Larger AFDs tend to require the construction of new chambers, which approximately doubles the price of installation.

A1.6   RELIABILITY/EFFECTIVENESS

About 75–80% of the respondents to the UKWIR survey[2] of sewerage undertakers considered anti-flooding devices to be either quite reliable or very reliable. The more modern designs (mostly plastic) were thought to be somewhat more reliable than older designs and easier to maintain. It is likely that many AFDs are never regularly maintained, but there was a fairly general consensus among the respondents that an appropriate maintenance interval is six months. Quantitative data on reliability are limited, but one sewerage undertaker with a total of 920 AFDs installed recorded only two definite and two possible flooding incidents associated with anti-flooding devices in a period of 12 months; these devices were serviced every six months.

Appendix A2 Technical data on pumping and vacuum systems

A2.1 PUMPING SYSTEMS

A2.1.1 Introduction

This appendix deals with wastewater pumping systems and makes particular mention of those types installed within premises. Although reference is made to the types of pumping installations most likely to be used in schemes for the prevention of flooding, there is no attempt to cover the huge variety of pumps and installation options available.

Pumping systems for dealing with sewer flooding problems can be considered in three categories of size and complexity.

(1) Packaged systems consisting of pumps and storage chambers that can take gravity flow from a group of properties and, if necessary, pump it under pressure into a surcharged public sewer.

(2) Intermediate-size pumps installed in inspection chambers that can discharge flow from a single property or basement into a surcharged sewer.

(3) Small macerating pumps contained in a collection tank installed in bathrooms or kitchens that can discharge flow from individual rooms under pressure through small-bore pipework; higher-rated units are able to pump from below ground level to above the surcharge level in drains and sewers (either directly or via gravity pipework).

A2.1.2 Types of pumps

Submersible centrifugal pumps, which rotate at high speed and pressurise the water by centrifugal force, are the most common type of pump. There are three main types of centrifugal pumps:

- **vortex impeller** – general-purpose non-clogging pump with good solids handling. A vortex impeller creates a whirlpool or vortex inside the pump volute; solids pass through the vortex rather than through the impeller

- **channel impeller** – provides efficient pumping but with limited solids handling, and therefore suitable for lightly contaminated water only

- **grinder pump** – cuts solids into very small pieces that can be pumped though small-bore (typically 40 mm diameter) pipework without blockage. Suitable for low pumping rates (ie flows up to about 5 l/s). Often used in conjunction with a channel impeller.

Submersible centrifugal pumps are available in "explosion-proof" versions that do not create sparks etc that could initiate an explosion. Unless gases or flammable liquids are expected, explosion-proof pumps are not usually required in smaller installations.

Special materials are available to minimise corrosion. These are not normally used for small installations as it tends to be more cost effective to use standard pumps and to accept that they will have a shorter life.

As well as centrifugal pumps, some pumping systems feature other types of pumping device:

- **Positive displacement pumps**

  These pumps "screw" the wastewater into the pumping main. They operate at low speeds, leading to low wear and long life; they also produce high suction lift, which allows them to be installed above the sewage flow to facilitate maintenance. They have good solids handling characteristics, especially when fitted with a grinder. Therefore these pumps have a number of advantages over submersible centrifugal pumps but are considerably more expensive.

- **Pneumatic ejectors**

  Wastewater flows into a vessel; once it is full the contents are ejected into the pumping main by compressed air. They have the following advantages: good solids handling; well suited to low flow rates; no odour problems; low maintenance due to few moving parts; intrinsically safe in explosive atmospheres; and high reliability (with duplicate compressors). In the past, ejectors were probably the most commonly used method of wastewater pumping within buildings but nowadays are seldom used because of their high cost. They are also relatively noisy.

Pumps are frequently purchased on the basis of availability and capital cost alone. However, when selecting a pumping device, consideration should be given to:

- technical suitability for the proposed application (including provision of self-cleansing velocity of over 0.7 m/s in the discharge pipework, prevention of septicity)

- likely nature of wastewater inflows

- whole-life costs (cost of maintenance is often considerably greater than the initial cost)

- ease and frequency of maintenance

- standardisation

- risk of failure (probability and consequence)

- need for complete enclosure

- nuisance (noise and odour).

A2.1.3   European/British Standards (see Bibliography)

Wastewater pumping outside buildings is covered by BS EN 1761 and BS EN 752: Part 6, which supersedes BS 8301 and BS 8005: Part 2. In addition, where external pumping stations serving a group of properties are to be adopted by the sewerage undertaker, they may be required to comply with *Sewers for Adoption*[11].

A draft European Standard, prEN 12056 Part 4, has been prepared by Technical Committee TC 165/WG 21/TG 4 covering the layout and hydraulic design of effluent pumping systems installed inside buildings. If it receives favourable votes from sufficient European countries, it is expected to come into force in 1999. Current German national regulations require inhabited basements below the expected flood level of the public sewer (usually taken as road or pavement level at the point of connection) to be drained using pumped systems.

European Standard BS EN 1671 deals with "Pressure sewerage systems outside buildings".

A2.1.4   Application

Ofwat accepts that the installation of a suitable packaged pumping system can provide a permanent solution of a sewer-flooding problem and enable the property to be removed from the at-risk register in DG5.

Draft European Standard prEN 12056-4 requires sanitary appliances located below the expected flood level of a sewer to be protected against backflow by installation of a pump, with discharge pipework arranged to lift flow above the flood level before discharge to a sewer (referred to as a "backflow loop"). However, it also permits sanitary appliances located below flood level in little-used rooms to be protected from backflow by an anti-flooding device conforming to the requirements in the European Standard currently being drafted (see Appendix A1).

A2.1.5   Reliability/effectiveness

The use of mechanical plant means that these systems must be considered less reliable and effective than the equivalent gravity system. However, modern pumping equipment and valves are used extensively and have established a good record for reliability, particularly where duplicate pumps and/or emergency storage is incorporated.

A2.1.6   Pumping inside buildings

Wastewater lifting plants within buildings are covered by draft European Standard prEN12056: Part 4, which provides guidance on specification and selection. Product specifications for small wastewater lifting plants are covered by draft European Standard prEN 12050: Parts 1 to 4.

Until the final versions of these standards are published, there is little alternative but to reference proprietary systems and manufacturers' installation instructions.

There are many different types of pump and a large number of suppliers covering a wide range of lifting plant that are able to deal with flows from individual sanitary appliances or from an entire property.

A2.1.7   Small pumping stations outside buildings

Pumps can be installed in alternative ways:

- **Guide rail coupling**. This provides a remote-operated, quick-release coupling to permanent pipework. It needs a special coupling on the pipework securely anchored to the sump.

- **Freestanding**. The pump has its own support and uses a flexible hose. No sump preparation is needed and it is relatively cheap.

- **Dry**. The pump is mounted outside the wet sump; it is generally applicable to positive-displacement pumps that are installed above the pump sump.

Pumps may either be installed in an existing or purpose-built sump or provided as a complete packaged pumping station (normally comprising a GRP sump, pumps, pipework, valves and controls).

A2.1.8 Large pumping stations outside buildings

Larger pumping stations, typical of installations that are adopted by sewerage undertakers, should comply with Sewers for Adoption[11].

A2.2 VACUUM SYSTEMS

A2.2.1 Description

Vacuum sewerage systems rely on a vacuum to transport sewage. A vacuum is induced and maintained in the pipe system by central vacuum pumps and a reservoir. Conventional gravity drains connect one or more properties to a sewage-collection chamber. When the sewage reaches a preset level, a pneumatic "interface" valve opens and the contents of the chamber are sucked into the vacuum line. When the chamber is almost empty the valve closes.

Vacuum systems for drainage inside buildings are also available. These are similar to the systems used on board ships and aeroplanes and normally are installed where routing of traditional sanitary pipework is a problem or water is at a premium. However, they can be used to drain areas of buildings below flood level and discharge wastewater at a higher level. The advantages of such a system lie in convenient drainage of appliances located in isolated positions around the building using only a single vacuum station.

A2.2.2 European/British Standards (see Bibliography)

Vacuum sewerage systems outside buildings are covered by BS EN 1091. However, successful operation of much of the system depends on proprietary products (particularly the interface valves) to the extent that specialist suppliers and/or contractors should be consulted to confirm specific design data.

Vacuum drainage systems inside buildings are covered by a draft BS EN, which is being prepared.

A2.2.3 Types of application

Vacuum systems can be used to bring sewerage to difficult areas where costs and construction difficulties had previously prevented construction of conventional gravity systems. They can also be used for problem areas in large communities, hospitals and housing estates, as well as to separate and isolate areas susceptible to back-flooding from an existing sewerage network, so that they can be drained independently with flows discharged back into the network at more appropriate locations.

A2.2.5   Extent of usage

Vacuum sewerage systems are used in a limited number of "public sewerage" applications in flat terrain, most notably in parts of East Anglia, and more commonly within individual private developments of various sizes.

The number of vacuum systems used inside buildings in the UK is small.

A2.2.6   Costs

The ability to use plastic pipes laid in narrow trenches at minimum cover – and with no manholes on the vacuum system – can significantly reduce costs. Significant additional cost advantages can be gained in flat terrain, high water tables, and unstable or rock conditions. These potential savings have to be set against the costs of the vacuum plant and interface valves, together with ongoing operating and maintenance costs.

A2.2.7   Reliability/effectiveness

The use of mechanical plant and the fundamental need to maintain vacuum conditions mean that these systems have to be considered as being less reliable and effective than the equivalent gravity system. However, should there be a requirement to drain an area separately from an existing sewer that is susceptible to flooding, then vacuum systems merit detailed consideration.

Appendix A3 Technical data on sewerage options

A3.1   LOCAL STRUCTURAL IMPROVEMENTS

A3.1.1   Description

A cause of surcharging in sewers can be local restrictions or other sources of avoidable head loss that produce backing up of flow in the upstream direction.

Unsupervised connections often result in laterals intruding into sewers, and these can significantly reduce sewer capacity and also lead to blockages. This type of fault can be identified by CCTV surveying and be rectified using remote techniques.

Another common problem that can cause very severe reductions in flow capacity is poor benching in chambers. Re-benching a chamber to improve its hydraulic performance is relatively inexpensive and can achieve significant improvements.

Where hydraulic modelling suggests that hydraulic capacity is adequate but experience indicates otherwise, the possibility of a localised problem should be considered. Although CCTV surveying will reveal intruding connections, flow survey data or, preferably, visual inspection during times of high flow may be required to identify problems. Once identified, remedial works are generally quite simple to design.

A3.1.2   European/British Standards (see Bibliography)

The various components of these types of solutions are covered in BS EN 752 and the many guidelines covering the planning, design and construction of new sewerage facilities.

A3.1.3   Types of application

This option can be a potential solution to many sewer-flooding problems and directly addresses the cause of the problem.

A3.1.4   Extent of usage

This option is probably not used extensively because of difficulties in identifying problems.

A3.1.5   Costs

Capital costs tend to be low, and routine maintenance costs may also be reduced as a result. However, investigation costs may be relatively high.

A3.1.6   Reliability/effectiveness

If such solutions are properly planned and designed, they are generally reliable and effective; they are therefore normally "low-cost".

A3.2 REDUCTION/ATTENUATION OF SURFACE WATER INFLOWS AND REDUCTION OF INFILTRATION

A3.2.1 Description

This option comprises techniques aimed at attenuating or reducing inflows into a sewerage system. Many are widely recognised as source control or best management practice (BMP) techniques. Examples include: attenuation of roof runoff; disconnection of paved areas; disconnection of roof areas; and reductions in the number, or rate of inflow, of gullies or other stormwater inlets. Other methods include reduction of infiltration into the network, and identification and correction of malconnections.

A3.2.2 European/British Standards

No Standards have been identified that deal with this group of options. However, individual design guides cover many of the particular techniques.

A3.2.3 Types of application

There are many ways in which these techniques can be used. They include: use of water butts; implementation of BMP techniques; redirection of small watercourses; repair/fitting of tide flaps to prevent high river or tide levels causing backflow into sewerage systems; reduction of groundwater infiltration; redirection of surface water, or reduction in its rate of inflow to separate foul systems.

A3.2.4 Extent of usage

Methods of reducing inflow of surface water to sewers have not been widely used in the UK to date, but BMP techniques are starting to be actively promoted by the various environmental agencies.

A3.2.5 Costs

The costs of the different techniques vary, but potentially they are highly cost-effective, particularly when viewed on a catchment-wide basis.

A3.2.6 Reliability/effectiveness

The reliability and effectiveness of these techniques must be judged on a project-specific basis, but the opportunities are significant. Potential problems are assignment of maintenance responsibilities, correction of failures and cross-agency/institutional issues.

A3.3 BETTER USE OF EXISTING STORAGE IN SEWERAGE SYSTEM

A3.3.1 Description

The general techniques for making better use of existing storage in sewerage systems are not fully exploited as yet. Passive and active methods may be used.

Most applications in the UK to date have been of the passive type. An example is the addition of flow control devices in the upstream part of a system to make use of storage capacity in manholes and thereby reduce peak flows farther downstream.

Active types of solution involve interaction between flow conditions and the operation of equipment such as pumps, gates and off-line storage tanks. The interaction may be achieved by operations staff applying written rules based on past experience, perhaps supported by analysis of the system's behaviour using a hydraulic model. Alternatively, the operating rules may be implemented automatically by means of electronic links between the flow control equipment and sensors located at key points in the system.

In the next generation of solutions, full real-time control may become an option. In this, a computer model forecasts flow conditions in the sewerage system and evaluates alternative strategies for operation of the control equipment; this type of option will normally tend to be applicable only on a catchment-wide basis. An example of a possible application is the linking of the operation of pumping stations to flood predictions obtained from a network of rain-gauges. If a major storm were developing, it might be decided to increase pumping in advance so as to draw down water levels in the sewerage system and thereby increase the amount of available storage.

A3.3.2   European/British Standards

No relevant Standards have been identified.

A3.3.3   Types of application

The use of active and passive control is currently envisaged as being able to provide the following benefits:

- reduction or prioritisation of flooding
- reduction or prioritisation of spills from CSOs
- reduced pumping costs
- reduced treatment costs
- reduced maintenance costs
- deferment of capital expenditure
- indirect benefits.

The catchment-wide planning and design of such schemes can potentially make a major contribution to the tackling of sewer-flooding problems.

A3.3.4   Extent of usage

At present, specific local solutions are considered on an ad-hoc basis. The potential benefits (and limitations) of managing and controlling flows within sewerage systems are just beginning to be recognised, although they have not yet been exploited.

A3.3.5   Costs

There is little current information on costs. However, initial indications are that total catchment solutions aimed at the better management and use of existing systems are likely to be very cost-effective. In the case of active systems, the need for additional telemetry is more likely to affect operational expenditure than capital expenditure.

A3.3.6 Reliability/effectiveness

Specific information is not available, but these issues are being addressed as part of current research.

A3.4 OVERFLOWS OR REDIRECTION OF FLOWS WITHIN SYSTEM

A3.4.1 Description

External overflows, bifurcations or diversions, can be located at points of hydraulic overloading to remove excess flows from the sewerage system. External overflows are generally designated as combined sewer overflows (CSOs) and entail discharge to a surface water sewer, land drain or watercourse. Diversions, together with bifurcations, are used to divert excess flows either into another part of the same system with spare capacity or into an adjacent system.

A3.4.2 European/British Standards (see Bibliography)

BS EN 752 covers the various components of these types of solution, and also deals with the guidelines and regulatory frameworks that cover the planning, design and construction of such facilities.

A3.4.3 Types of application

The use of permanent external overflows is now only generally considered as part of a catchment-wide strategy, rather than being directed at the protection of individual properties. Temporary consents for storm overflows may be considered as a temporary solution to prevent the flooding of properties. Internal overflows or redirection of flows from one part of a system to another can allow for better use of an existing system.

A3.4.4 Extent of usage

In the current regulatory environment, the construction of a new combined sewer overflow (CSO) is unlikely to receive a permanent discharge consent from the appropriate environment agency without extensive mitigation works. Factors that would be taken into account in each case are the receiving water quality, the degree of dilution and the amenity value of the watercourse. However, under certain circumstances, CSOs, or rationalisation of CSOs, may be permitted as a temporary expedient to prevent properties being flooded from sewers; these would be reviewed on a case-by-case basis.

A3.4.5 Costs

The capital costs of various ancillary facilities (storage zone, stilling zone and screening, if required) and other mitigating measures usually make this option quite expensive. The sensitive nature of these installations, together with the increasing use of associated mechanical plant, means that the operating and maintenance costs also need to be considered.

A3.4.6   Reliability/effectiveness

The performance of CSOs can be sensitive to the setting of the overflow levels. Properly planned, designed and managed CSOs are effective and reliable means of reducing incidents of sewer flooding. However, they create another set of issues to be addressed in terms of discharge consents and pollution control.

A3.5   PROVISION OF STORAGE AND USE OF FLOW CONTROLS

A3.5.1   Description

Together with construction work to increase sewer capacity, this is the most commonly used method of solving flooding problems. Flows in the downstream system are controlled to the capacity of the pipes by storing excess flows until the system can cope. This may entail the provision of purpose-built storage to attenuate flows, usually in the form of on-line or off-line detention tanks. Flow control devices are used to control the onward flow to the downstream part of the system and/or to divert flows into storage.

A3.5.2   European/British Standards (see Bibliography)

The various components of this type of solution are covered in BS EN 752, together with the many guidelines covering the planning, design and construction of new sewerage facilities.

A3.5.3   Types of application

This option has traditionally been considered as a potential solution to most kinds of sewer-flooding problem. The increasing use of numerical flow-simulation models means that this type of solution can be judged against a number of technical and financial criteria. However, there is increasing awareness that storage can be expensive in relation to its benefits and that storage solutions are sensitive to modelling assumptions and/or errors. Storage can be particularly appropriate in the downstream parts of systems as a means of allowing other capital investments to be delayed. However, in many cases, although the problem may occur downstream, the solution lies upstream. Storage at the upper end of a system, with a flow control, may be cheaper than conventional large tanks at the downstream end. Storage used to reduce CSO discharges can also be used to reduce problems at properties, thereby providing dual benefits and cost savings.

A3.5.4   Extent of usage

Downstream storage is a traditional solution, now subject to more careful technical and financial appraisal when adopting a catchment-wide approach. Upstream flow control and provision of supplementary storage has been used successfully in the USA to provide effective alleviation of flooding from surcharged combined sewers.

A3.5.5   Costs

Downstream storage schemes tend to be capital-intensive solutions, coupled with on-going operational and maintenance commitments. Nonetheless, if several properties are affected by flooding, such solutions can offer benefits of scale. A financial assessment would need to be made against the maximum allowable cost for dealing with sewer flooding. This allowable cost varies between sewerage undertakers, and is dictated by asset management plans and other external factors such as customer care. Budgetary provisions for operation and maintenance costs will also need to be considered. Where the configuration of the sewerage system permits the use of flow controls to mobilise latent storage, significant cost savings can be realised (see also Section A3.4).

A3.5.6   Reliability/effectiveness

Such solutions, when properly planned, designed and managed, are generally reliable and effective and can be "low-cost". Issues that need to be considered are: the sensitivity of the required storage volume to the design assumptions; the filling and emptying modes of the tanks; access and maintenance; grit deposition; ventilation; and the dangers of small-aperture flow control devices becoming blocked. Grit separators have been used upstream of large storage tanks to reduce maintenance requirements. Provision of upstream controls with supplementary storage tends to result in smaller tanks or storage structures that can be more easily designed to be self-cleansing.

A3.6   CONSTRUCTION WORKS TO INCREASE SEWER CAPACITY

A3.6.1   Description

Together with the provision of storage, this is the most commonly used method of solving sewer-flooding problems. With this option, major parts of existing systems are replaced or enhanced to remove the hydraulic restrictions that are causing surcharging or flooding. There is a significant potential risk that a problem may be moved farther downstream unless the design of the proposed improvements are checked all the way through the system to the outfall or treatment works.

Capital-intensive schemes to reduce flooding should not be carried out in isolation. They should be assessed on a catchment-wide basis, and the opportunity taken to investigate the potential to improve receiving water quality by reducing the number and frequency of storm discharges. Similarly, any other operational shortcomings of the system should be addressed at the same time.

A3.6.2   European/British Standards (see Bibliography)

The various components of these types of solutions are covered in BS EN 752, together with the many guidelines covering the planning, design and construction of new sewerage facilities.

A3.6.3   Types of application

This option is traditionally considered as a potential solution to most sewer-flooding problems. The option also offers the opportunity to deal with structural problems in the sewerage system. The likely expense and the disruption to the public, coupled with the risk of merely transferring a problem elsewhere, mean that this option is viewed with more circumspection now. The increasing use of numerical flow-simulation models allows this type of solution to be tested and judged against a number of technical and financial criteria. Under certain circumstances, these solutions can offer good-value/low-cost schemes when assessed against the costs of protecting individual properties against flooding. It should also be noted that storage, and some other options described above, may not reduce the frequency with which a system surcharges.

A3.6.4 Extent of usage

This is a traditional and widely used solution that is now subject to more careful technical and financial appraisal when catchment-wide approaches are being applied.

A3.6.5 Costs

This type of solution tends to be very capital-intensive, and is usually also expensive and disruptive. Nonetheless, if a number of properties are affected by flooding this option can offer benefits of scale. A financial assessment needs to be made taking account of the maximum allowable cost for preventing sewer flooding at the at-risk properties; other benefits that may be achieved at the same time should also be included. This allowable cost varies between sewerage undertakers, and is dictated by asset management plans and other external factors such as levels of customer service.

A3.6.6 Reliability/effectiveness

Such solutions, when properly planned and designed, are generally reliable and effective and can be "low-cost". A "new" scheme can also offer the opportunity to address other shortcomings in the sewerage system, such as structural problems.

A3.7 PRO-ACTIVE MAINTENANCE

A3.7.1 Description

This is maintenance work carried out in a planned way at key points in a sewerage system to ensure that the hydraulic capacity is not reduced by blockages or by the build-up of sediment deposits or excessive sliming in the pipes.

A3.7.2 European/British Standards

No relevant Standards have been identified. Most of the individual techniques are covered in guidance or best practice manuals.

A3.7.3 Types of application

Information from operational records and databases, together with results from numerical flow models, can be used to direct maintenance activities to "hot spots" (eg sediment-endangered sewers or areas with a history of sewer blockages).

A3.7.4 Extent of usage

This option is becoming more common due to the increased availability of operational and asset information with which to make informed decisions.

A3.7.5 Costs

The costs of pro-active maintenance vary, and have to be viewed against the sewerage undertaker's own operational philosophy. The costs depend upon individual financial management regimes, regulatory requirements and individual/corporate perceptions.

Unlike most of the other options considered in this report, the costs of pro-active maintenance are borne by maintenance budgets rather than capital budgets. Accounting methods ought not to prevent the adoption of this option if it is the best solution for a particular problem and represents the most effective use of resources.

A3.7.6   Reliability/effectiveness

Monitoring of the results of the maintenance work must be carried out to determine its effectiveness and, if necessary, to adjust the frequency of cleaning.

A3.8   WALLS OR BUNDS

A3.8.1   Description

This option involves the construction of a wall or bund around a single property, or a group of properties, to provide protection from sewer flooding. In cases of garden flooding, a wall may be built around a manhole or inspection chamber to limit the extent of surface flooding.

A3.8.2   European/British Standards

No relevant Standards have been identified.

A3.8.3   Types of application

Applications tend to be site-specific and should primarily be assessed on the basis of: relative levels; the degree of interference such a solution would have on pedestrian and vehicular access; and the general occupation and amenity of the property. This option is normally appropriate only when short-term solutions are needed.

A3.8.4   Extent of usage

Examples of walls constructed around properties to prevent flooding from sewers are very few in the UK. However, walls have been built to contain surface flooding away from properties, and raising of manhole covers is often used to prevent local flooding. Bunds have been placed around low foul sewerage manholes to contain flooding at low points and prevent further pollution.

A3.8.5   Costs

Building walls and raising manhole covers can be low-cost solutions, although the costs of any other accommodation works and compensations should also be considered.

A3.8.6   Reliability/effectiveness

Such measures may be considered as reasonably reliable when considered as temporary solutions to flooding problems. However, they will usually have been designed using historic and/or anecdotal evidence and hence will not have been subject to rigorous analysis.

A3.9 PURCHASE OF PROPERTIES

A3.9.1 Description

This option involves the sewerage undertaker purchasing a property either to remove it from a list of occupied properties (eg the DG5 register) affected by flooding, or to change its use/method of occupation to mitigate the effects of flooding. For example, a residential property might be converted to an alternative use such as an amenity centre.

In some cases only the part of a property at risk of flooding might need to be purchased in order to change its use, eg an occupied basement could be closed and filled in.

A3.9.2 European/British Standards

No relevant Standards have been identified.

A3.9.3 Types of application

This option would normally only be considered on cost and customer service grounds if the costs of any alternative measures were to exceed the market value of the particular property.

A3.9.4 Extent of usage

Use of this option is extremely limited in the UK.

A3.9.5 Costs

The net cost is the purchase price of the property, together with compensation and relocation costs, offset by any revenue income from its reuse.

A3.9.6 Reliability/effectiveness

This option addresses the effects of sewer flooding, but not the causes.

Appendix A4 Comparisons of options for Cases A to D in Chapter 8

A4.1   GENERAL

In the following comparisons it is assumed that flooding occurs on average every five years (in Years 2, 7 and 12) and, for the purpose of this comparison only, that a discount rate of 7.5% and a discounting period of 15 years apply. It is also assumed that the benefit obtained from preventing flooding has a value of £4000 per event for an occupied property and £3000 for an occupied basement. Prices in the tables below are in pounds Sterling throughout.

A4.2   CASE A – EXAMPLE OF FLOODING IN A SINGLE BASEMENT

Table A.4.1   *Comparison of options to prevent flooding in a single basement*

Item	Anti-flooding device	Pumping	Purchase of property	Pro-active mainten-ance[8]
Purchase cost	300	300	60 000	nil
Installation cost	800[4]	200	200[5]	nil
Maintenance cost (pa)	50[2]	70[1, 2]	nil[3]	nil
Operational cost (pa)	nil	2[1]	nil[3]	300[9]
Value of benefit per event	3000[6]	3000[6]	3000[6]	3000[6]
Discounted cost	1541	1728[7]	60 200	3548
Discounted benefit	5664	5664	5664	5664
Net benefit/(cost)	4123	3936	(54 536)	2116
Reliability	Medium	Medium	High	High

Notes

1. This will be paid by the owner/occupier, not the sewerage undertaker, but has been included for comparison purposes only.
2. Assumes inspection, cleaning and any remedial work twice a year.
3. Assumes offset by alternative use.
4. Assumes modifications will be required to pipework.
5. Assumes disconnection of basement drainage.
6. Allowances made for cleaning and disinfection, replacement of carpets and other water-affected furniture, compensation, testing and remedial works to electrical system and compensation.
7. Assumes pump replaced every five years (as they are small units).
8. May not be appropriate or fully solve problem.
9. Assumes four maintenance visits in the first year and annually thereafter.

CASE B – EXAMPLE OF FLOODING OF A SINGLE PROPERTY

Table A4.2 *Comparison of options to prevent flooding in a single property*

Item	Anti-flooding device	Pumping	Purchase of property	Pro-active mainten-ance[9]	Wall or bund [9]
Purchase cost	300[8]	1000	120 000	nil	nil
Installation cost	1000[7]	1500	15 000[5]	nil	500
Maintenance cost pa	50[3]	100[4,3]	nil[1]	nil	nil
Operational cost pa	nil	10[2]	nil[1]	300[10]	nil
Value of benefit per event	4000[6]	4000[6]	4000[6]	4000[6]	4000[6]
Discounted cost	1741	3751	135 000	3548	500
Discounted benefit	7552	7552	7552	7552	7552
Net benefit/(cost)	5811	3801	(127 448)	4004	7052
Reliability	Medium	Medium	High	High	High

Notes

1. Assumes demolition of the property.
2. Probably borne by householder, but included for completeness.
3. Assumes inspection, cleaning and any remedial work twice a year.
4. Assumes pump replacement every 7.5 years.
5. Assumes demolition.
6. Allowance made for cleansing and disinfection, replacement of carpets and other water-affected furniture, testing and remedial work to electrical system and compensation.
7. Assumes no additional storage required and a single AFD in existing inspection chamber.
8. Simple type of anti-flooding device assumed (cost of powered type around £1200).
9. May not be appropriate or fully solve the problem.
10. Assumes four maintenance visits in the first year and annually thereafter.

A4.4 CASE C – EXAMPLE OF FLOODING OF PROPERTIES IN A SINGLE STREET

It is assumed in this example that 12 properties are to be protected from sewer flooding.

Table A4.3a *Comparison of options to prevent flooding of properties in a single street*

Item	Preventing backflow			Disconnection	
	AFDs (individual properties)	AFD (combined properties)	Pumping (individual properties)	Pumping (combined properties)	Bypass sewer[9]
Planning/ investigation cost	1500	1500	2500	2500	3000
Purchase cost	2400	600	10 000	2 000	50 000
Installation cost	8400[4]	17 400	15 000	10 000	nil
Maintenance cost pa	500[5]	50[5]	1000[5,7]	500[5,8]	10[6]
Operational cost pa	nil	nil	100	80	nil
Value of benefit per event[2]	48 000	48 000	48 000	48 000	48 000
Discounted cost	16 714	19 941	40 010	19 620	53 088
Discounted benefit[3]	90 624	90 624	90 624	90 624	90 624
Net benefit/(cost)	73 910	70 683	50 614	71 004	37 536
Net benefit/(cost) per property	6160	5890	4218	5917	3128
Reliability	Medium	Medium	Medium	Medium	High
Notes: See Table A4.3c.					

Table A4.3b *Comparison of options to prevent flooding of properties in a single street*

Item	Preventing/reducing surcharge				
	Construction works to increase sewer capacity	Pro-active mainten-ance[9]	Local structural improve-ments[9]	Reduction of surface water inflow[9]	Reduction of ground water inflow[9]
Planning/ investigation cost	3000[1]	1000	1500	5000	2500
Purchase cost	60 000	nil	2000	20 000	10 000
Installation cost	nil	nil	nil	nil	nil
Maintenance cost pa	10[6]	300[10]	nil	30[11]	30[11]
Operational cost pa	nil	nil	nil	nil	nil
Value of benefit per event[2]	48 000	48 000	48 000	48 000	48 000
Discounted cost	63 088	4548	3500	25 265	12 765
Discounted benefit[3]	90 624	90 624	90 624	90 624	90 624
Net benefit/(cost)	27 536	86 076	87 124	65 359	77 859
Net benefit/(cost) per property	2295	7173	7260	5447	6488
Reliability	High	High	High	High	High
Notes: See Table A4.3c.					

Table A4.3c   *Comparison of options to prevent flooding of properties in a single street*

Item	Preventing/reducing surcharge			
	Better use of existing storage[9]	Provision of storage[9]	Bypass sewer/ diversion[9]	CSO[9]
Planning/investigation cost	3000	3000	3000	3000
Purchase cost	2500	20 000	20 000	15 000
Installation cost	nil	nil	nil	nil
Maintenance cost pa	50	100	10	200
Operational cost pa	nil	nil	nil	nil
Value of benefit per event[2]	48 000	48 000	48 000	48 000
Discounted cost	5941	23 883	23 088	19 766
Discounted benefit[3]	90 624	90 624	90 624	90 624
Net benefit/cost	84 683	66 741	67 536	70 858
Net benefit/(cost) per property	7057	5562	5628	5905
Reliability	Medium	High	High	High

Notes

1. This assumes that a model/knowledge of the system already exists.
2. Assumes an average cost of £4000 per property for cleaning and disinfection, replacing carpets and other water-affected furniture, testing and remedial works to electrical system and compensation.
3. Assumes flooding every five years (in years 2,7 and 12).
4. Assumes no additional storage required and a single AFD can be fitted in existing inspection chamber.
5. Assumes an annual inspection and clean and any remedial work.
6. Assumes inspection and cleaning every 15 years.
7. Assumes pump replacement every 7.5 years (as smaller pumps used).
8. Assumes pump replacement every 15 years (as larger pumps used).
9. May not be appropriate or fully solve problem.
10. Assumes four maintenance visits in the first year and annually thereafter.
11. Assumes repeat inspections and remedial work.

CASE D – EXAMPLE OF FLOODING OF PROPERTIES ACROSS A SUB-CATCHMENT

It is assumed in this example that a total of 30 properties are to be protected from sewer flooding.

Table A4.4a   *Comparison of options to prevent flooding of properties across a sub-catchment*

Item	Individual AFDs[2]	Pumps for individual properties[2]	Pro-active maintenance	Better use of existing storage
Planning/ investigation cost	20 000	15 000	10 000	40 000[1]
Construction cost	27 000	65 000	nil	150 000
Maintenance cost pa	1500	3000	5000	100
Operational cost pa	nil	300	nil	nil
Value of benefit per event	120 000	120 000	120 000	120 000
Discounted cost	60 241	115 606	69 136	190 883
Discounted benefit	226 553	226 533	226 533	226 533
Net benefit/(cost)	166 312	110 927	157 397	35 650
Net benefit/(cost) per property	5544	3697	5247	1188
Reliability	Medium	Medium	High	High

Notes: See Table A4.4b.

Table A4.4b   *Comparison of options to prevent flooding of properties across a sub-catchment*

	Preventing/reducing surcharge		
	Construction works to increase sewer capacity	Provision of storage	CSO[2]
Planning/ investigation cost	30 000[1]	40 000	15 000
Construction cost	1 200 000	250 000	100 000
Maintenance cost pa	100	2500	1000
Operational cost pa	nil	nil	nil
Value of benefit per event	120 000	120 000	120 000
Discounted cost	1 230 883	312 068	123 827
Discounted benefit	226 533	226 533	226 533
Net benefit/(cost)	(1 004 350)	(85 535)	102 706
Net benefit/(cost) per property	(33 478)	(2851)	3424
Reliability	High	High	High

Notes

1. This assumes that a model/knowledge of the system already exists but includes modelling and verification of proposed solution.
2. Interim measures only.